WES
MONTGOMERY
for guitar tab

wise publications
london / new york / paris / sydney / copenhagen / madrid

exclusive distributors:

music sales limited
8/9 frith street,
london w1v 5tz, england

music sales pty limited
120 rothschild avenue,
rosebery, nsw 2018,
australia

order no. am937134
isbn 0-7119-5765-7
this book © copyright 1996 by wise publications

book design by michael bell design
compiled by peter evans
music arranged by andy jones
music processed by the pitts

printed in the united kingdom by
page bros limited, norwich, norfolk

photographs courtesy of
redferns and val wilmer

your guarantee of quality:
as publishers, we strive to produce every book to the
highest commercial standards

the music has been freshly engraved and the book has been
carefully designed to minimise awkward page turns and to make
playing from it a real pleasure

particular care has been given to specifying acid-free, neutral-sized
paper made from pulps which have not been elemental chlorine bleached
this pulp is from farmed sustainable forests and was produced with
special regard for the environment

throughout, the printing and binding have been planned to ensure a
sturdy, attractive publication which should give years of enjoyment

if your copy fails to meet our high standards, please inform us
and we will gladly replace it

music sales' complete catalogue describes thousands of titles and
is available in full colour sections by subject, direct from music sales limited.
please state your areas of interest and send a cheque/postal order for
£1.50 for postage to: music sales limited,
newmarket road, bury st. edmunds, suffolk ip33 3yb

visit the internet music shop at
http://www.musicsales.co.uk

airegin 6

besame mucho 16

blue 'n' boogie 26

dearly beloved 37

ecaroh 80

golden earrings 48

in your own sweet way 56

satin doll 62

the way you look tonight 68

whisper not 85

yesterdays 90

introduction 4

tablature & instructions explained 5

introduction

by andy jones

John L. 'Wes' Montgomery was born in Indianapolis, Indiana, on 6 March 1923. He started playing the guitar at the age of 19, moving quickly from a four-string guitar to the six-string model. His first influence was the great Charlie Christian.

Wes immediately set about transcribing Christian's recorded solos. One of his first gigs had him reproducing Christian's solos note for note. He wouldn't play anything else!

Wes lapped up information from colleagues and was soon working in his own right. By 1948 he was playing with Lionel Hampton's big band, but, ever the family man, he still operated around Indianapolis. In 1959 the great alto saxophonist Julian 'Cannonball' Adderley heard Wes one night and immediately decided to introduce him to a wider public.

On Cannonball's recommendation Wes secured a deal with Riverside, beginning an extremely fruitful collaboration which was to revolutionise jazz guitar. Later on he also recorded some fantastic music for the jazz label Verve. Wes was to encounter some criticism over some later recordings with orchestra which focused on lighter pop tunes, but even on these dates there's always something worth checking out. Wes died on 15 June 1968 after a heart attack.

Wes played with his right-hand thumb. He had amazing facility and could play things that few guitarists could come close to even with a plectrum. Wes plays fast eighth-note passages so strongly that he must have used both up and down strokes with his thumb. He also popularised the use of octaves in melodic playing – with fantastic command, as ever. One of the marks of a great player is that he can make very difficult passages sound effortless. Wes always had a strong sound on the instrument where many players lose a considerable amount of tone at fast tempos.

In rhythmic innovation Wes was right up to the minute. He was probably the first guitar player to really absorb the intricacies of rhythm cooked up by the more adventurous modern jazz drummers. He has the ability to really nail a heavy jazz eighth-note feel but he also plays rhythms which use odd groupings of beats, and he could even play all over the underlying pulse. Few guitar players have ever had this hip kind of feel. It's no surprise that John Coltrane asked Wes to be in his great band with Elvin Jones (Wes said no, thinking he wasn't up to the job).

Wes was a true improviser. You can hear this quite clearly by listening to out-takes from his records (many of the CD reissues of his albums come with out-takes as bonus tracks). His lines encompass bebop, blues and a free-wheeling approach to melodic improvising. He also had an extremely advanced sense of chord movement, often introducing sly chord substitutions into his treatments of standard tunes. His own tunes are full of hip jazz harmony. Check out 'Twisted Blues' from *'So Much Guitar'*.

Regarded as one of the finest jazz musicians on any instrument, Wes is still studied by all serious aspiring jazz guitarists.

tablature & instructions explained

The tablature stave comprises six lines, each representing a string on the guitar as illustrated.

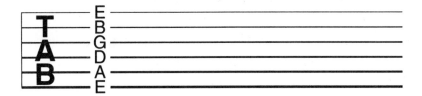

A number on any of the lines indicates, therefore, the string and fret on which a note should be played.

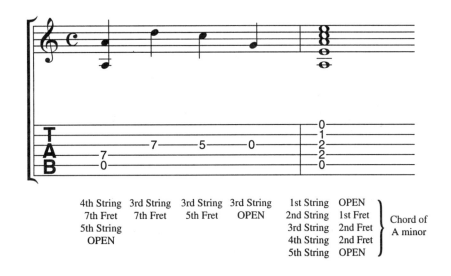

4th String	3rd String	3rd String	3rd String	1st String	OPEN	
7th Fret	7th Fret	5th Fret	OPEN	2nd String	1st Fret	
5th String				3rd String	2nd Fret	} Chord of
OPEN				4th String	2nd Fret	A minor
				5th String	OPEN	

Symbols Used

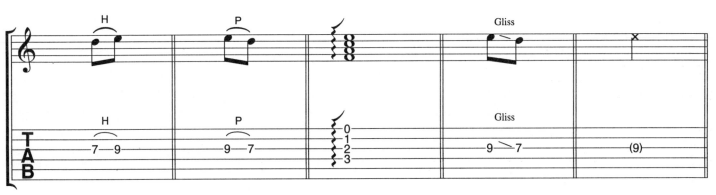

HAMMER-ON	PULL-OFF	RAKE-UP	GLISSANDO	CROSS-HEAD
Hammer a finger down on the next note without striking the string again.	Pull your finger off the string with a plucking motion to sound the next note without striking the string again.	Strum the notes upwards in the manner of an arpeggio.	Strike the note, then slide the finger up or down the fretboard as indicated.	This note-head indicates the string is to be totally muted to produce a percussive effect.

airegin

by sonny rollins

Sonny Rollins's 'Airegin' (the title is Nigeria backwards) provides a perfect vehicle for Wes. Note his use of repetitive rhythms. This kind of motivic improvising gives shape to a solo. This solo is jam packed with classic jazz vocabulary – it is basically a free lesson from one of the greatest improvisers ever. Wes ends the solo with octaves. If you're new to this device, don't be impatient; it takes a little getting used to.

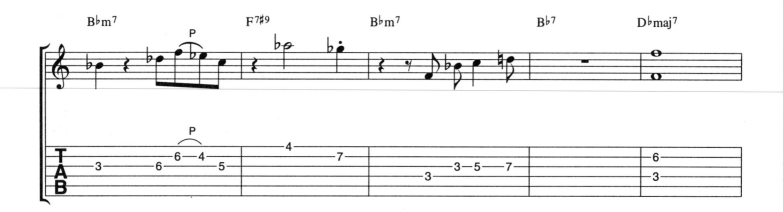

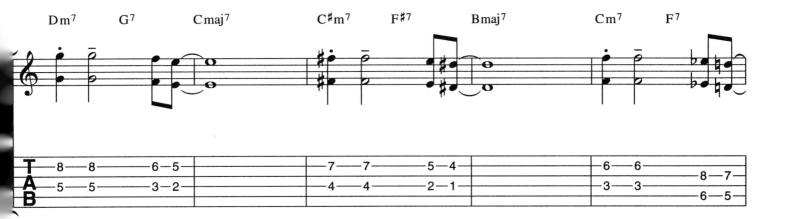

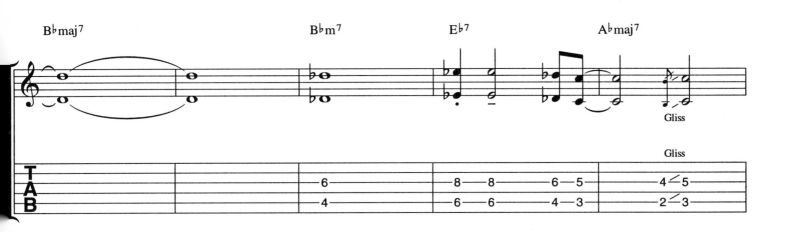

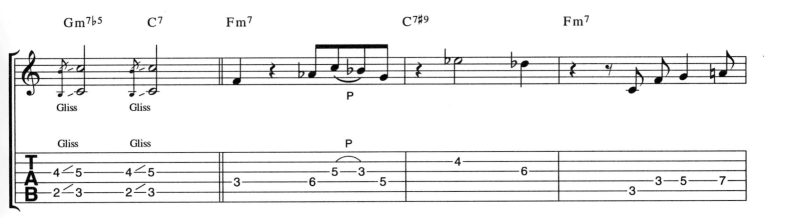

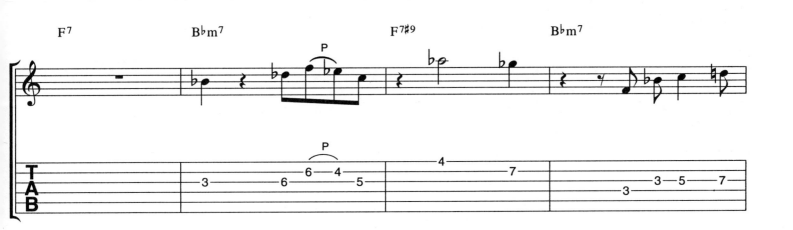

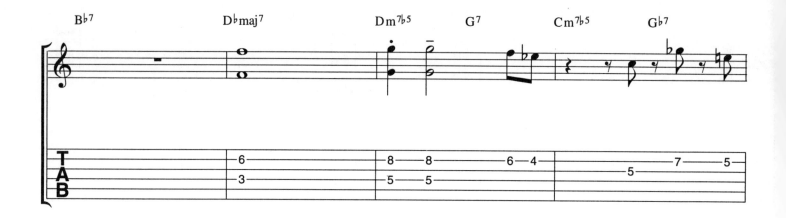

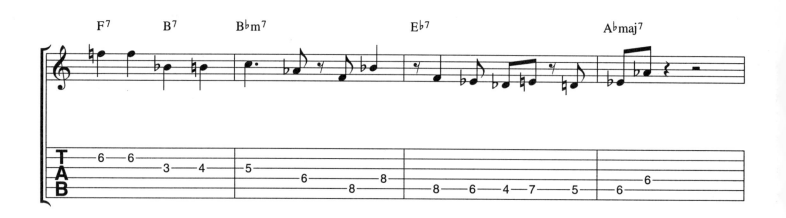

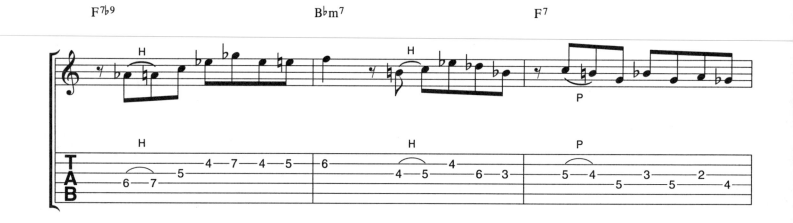

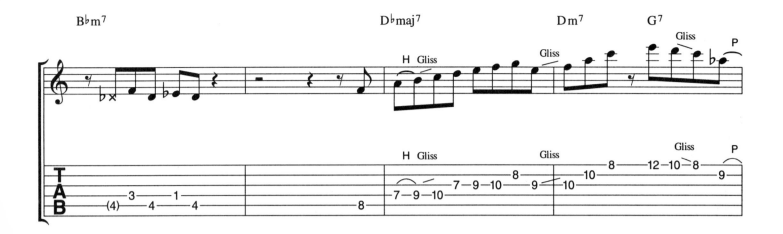

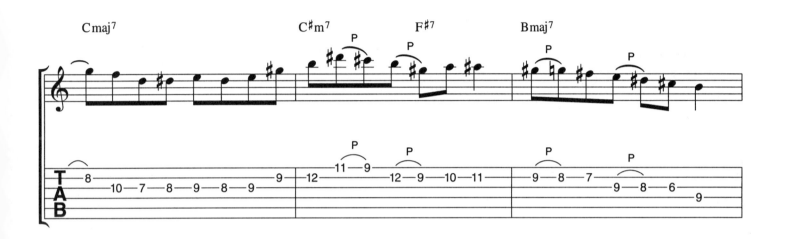

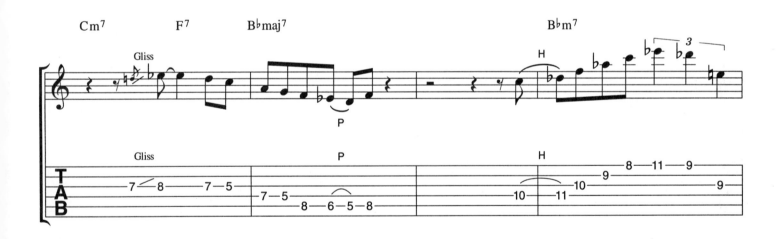

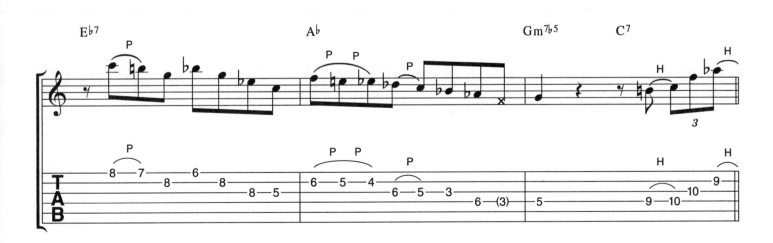

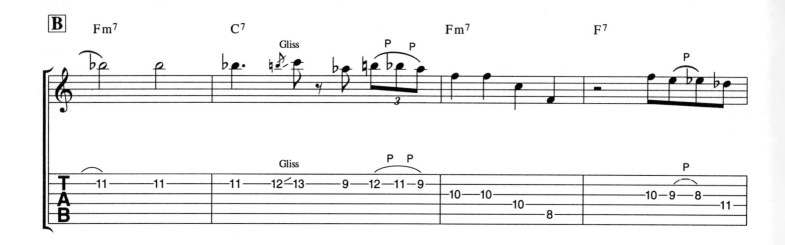

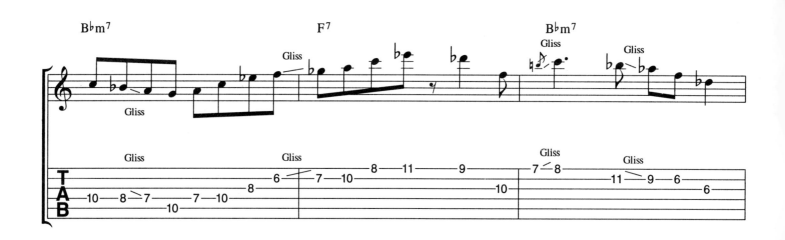

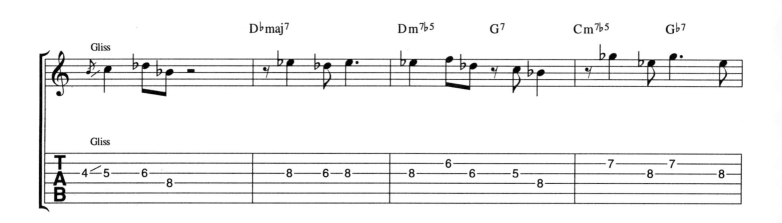

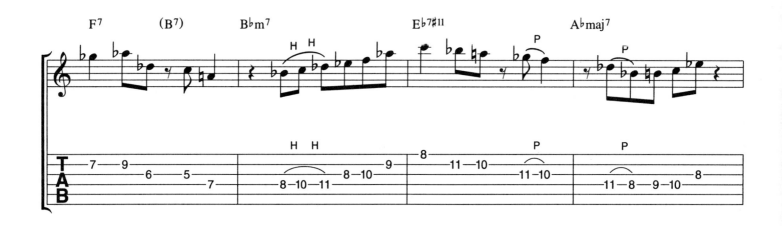

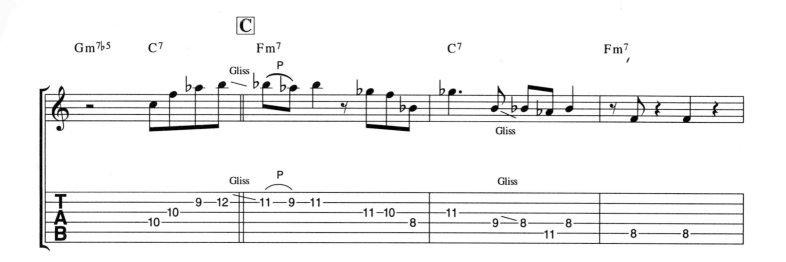

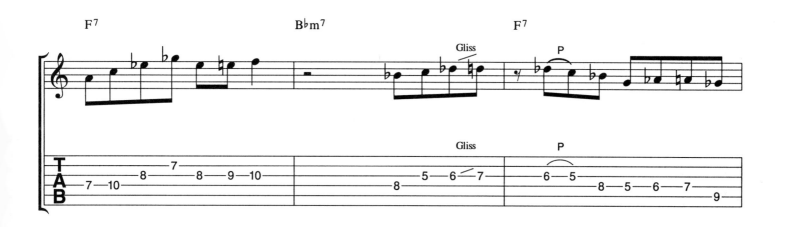

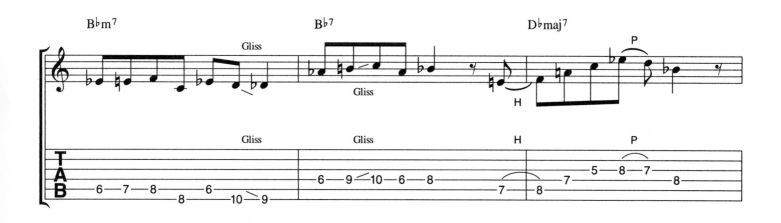

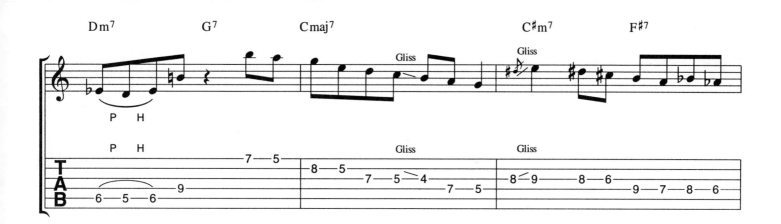

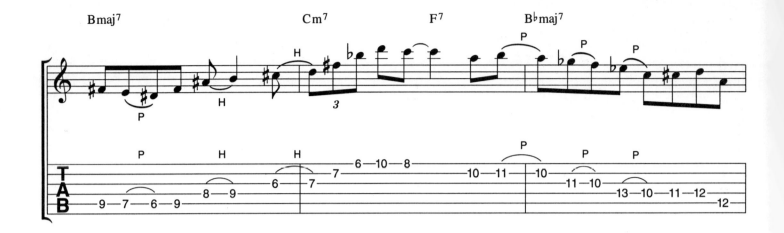

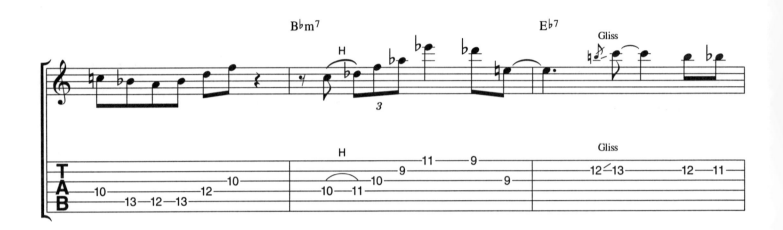

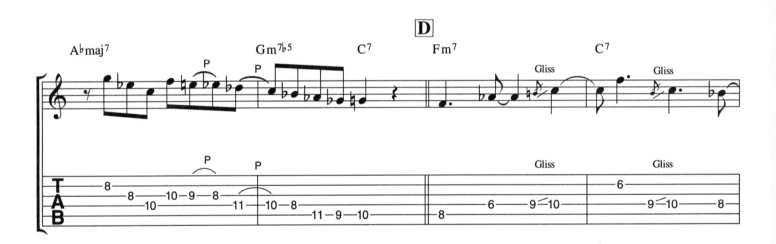

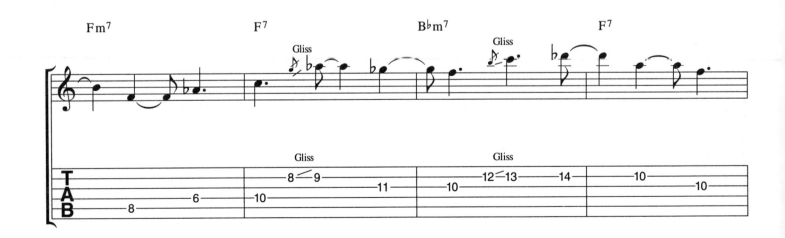

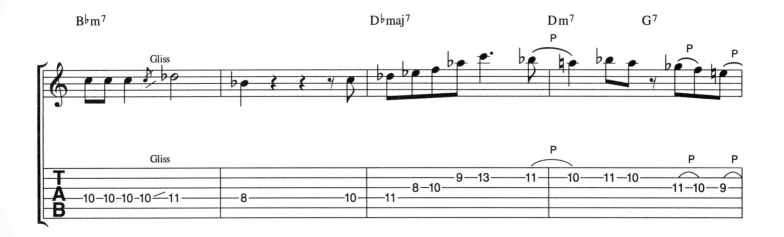

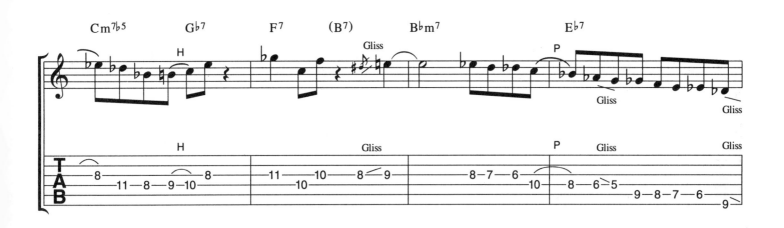

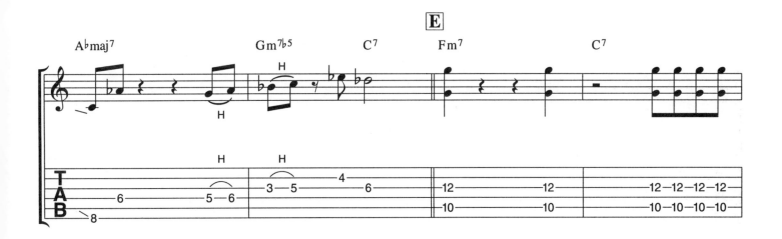

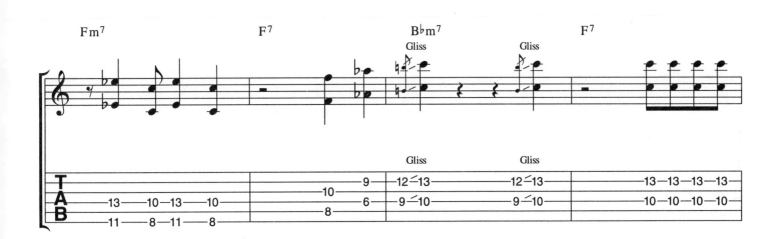

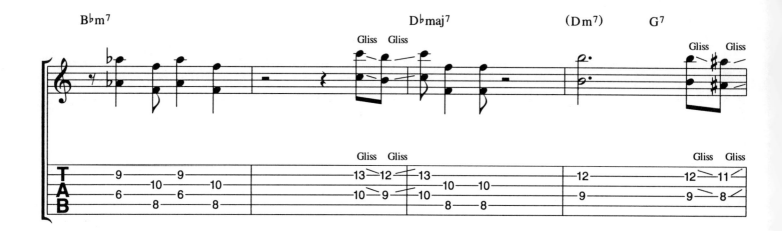

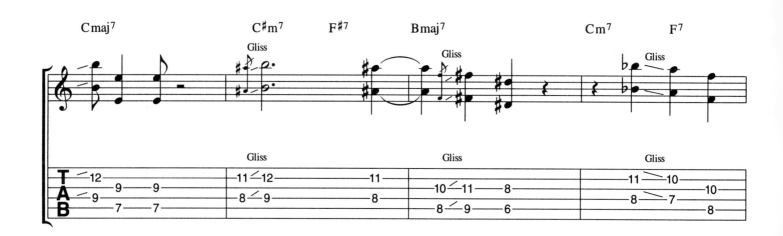

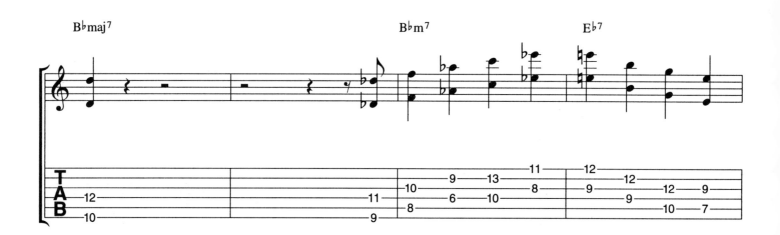

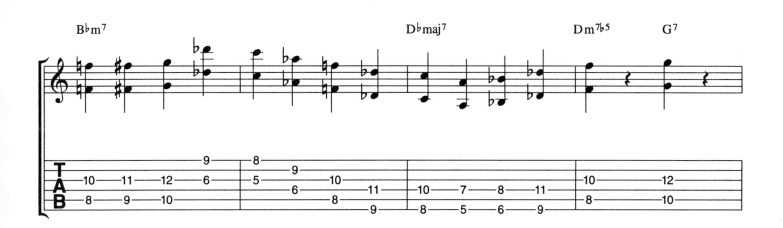

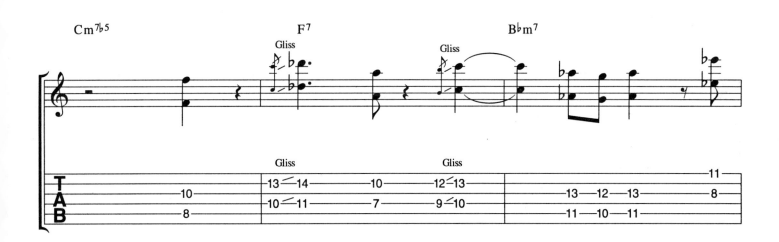

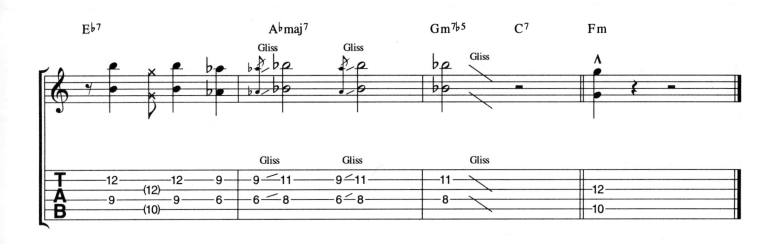

besame mucho

english words by sunny skylar
music by consuelo velazquez

Wes treats the melody of 'Besame Mucho' very freely. The first sections of the melody have very different fills and embellishments on the repeats (only the first time is written here). You'll note that the tune has an extremely long form – the first sections of the melody are 32 bars long, while the second section is 16 bars. This solo is a great introduction to improvising jazz in ¾ time. Wes plays some great lines here – try learning a few. If you're interested in other examples, check out Wes's solo on his own composition 'West Coast Blues' (available in *Greatest Jazz Solos For Guitar Tab* from Music Sales).

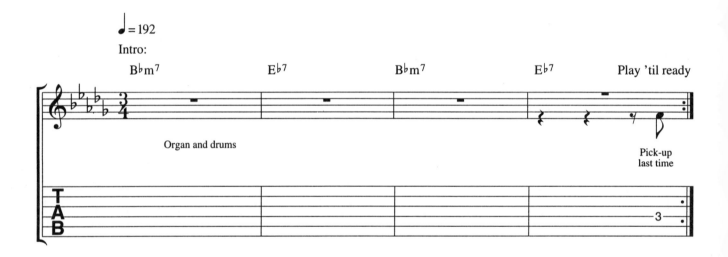

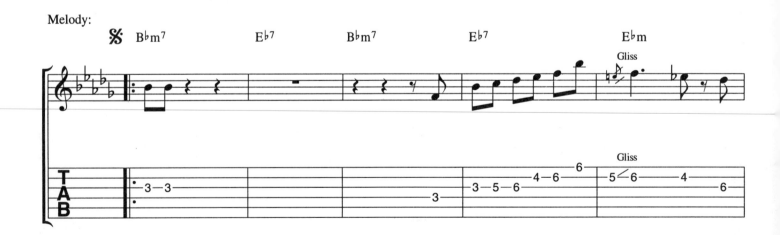

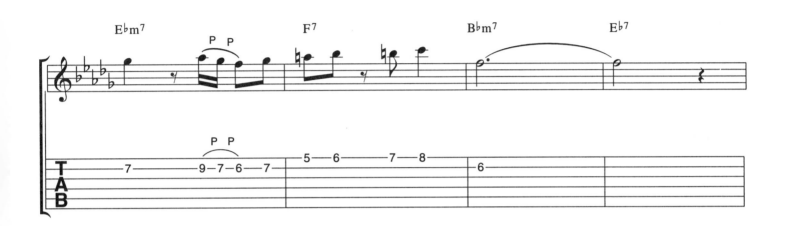

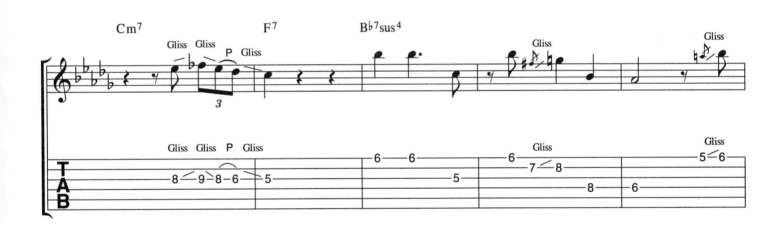

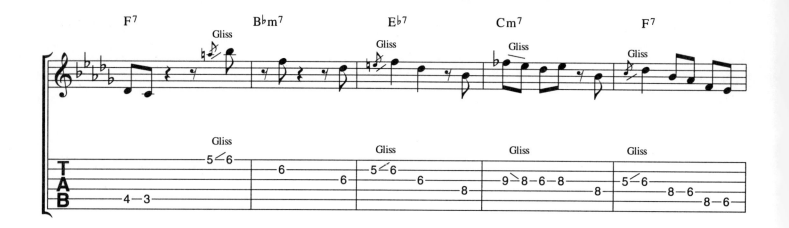

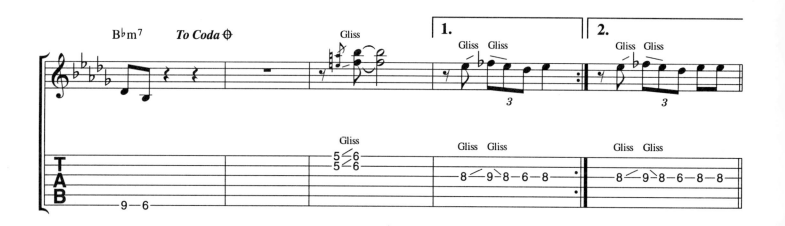

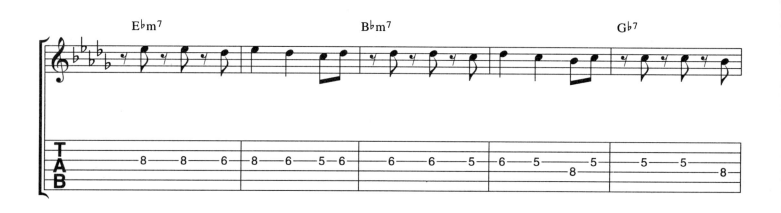

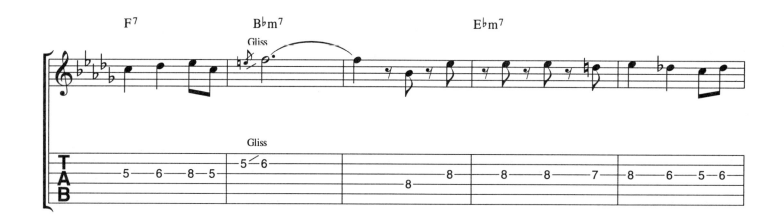

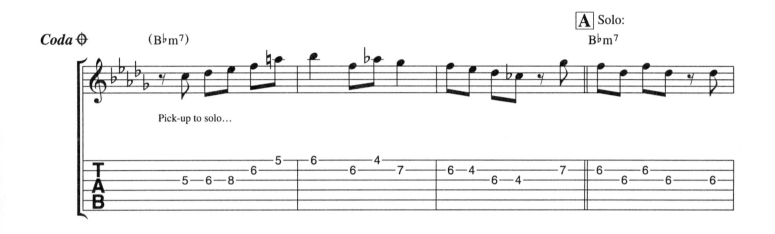

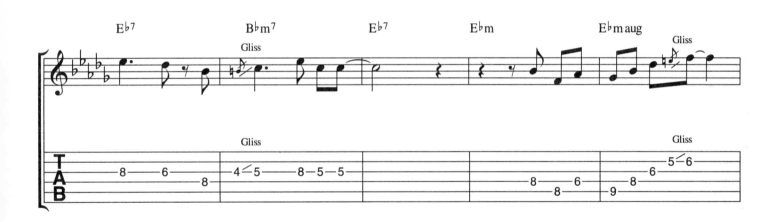

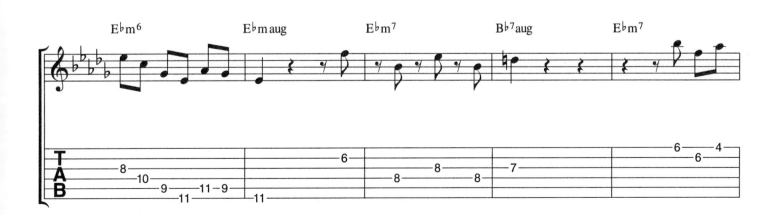

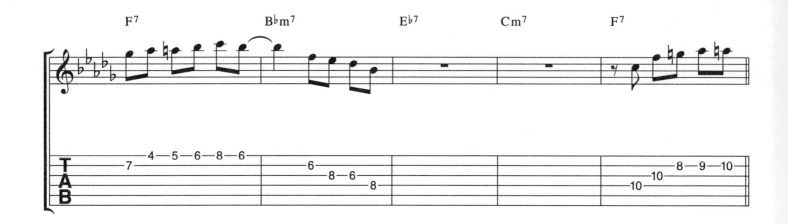

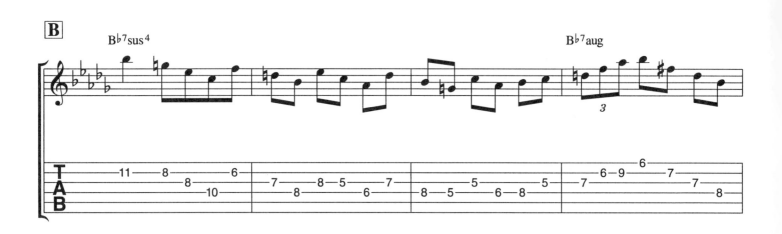

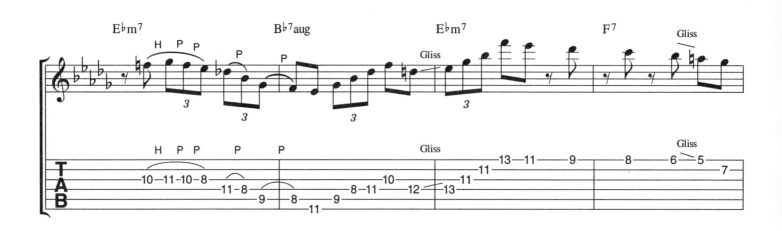

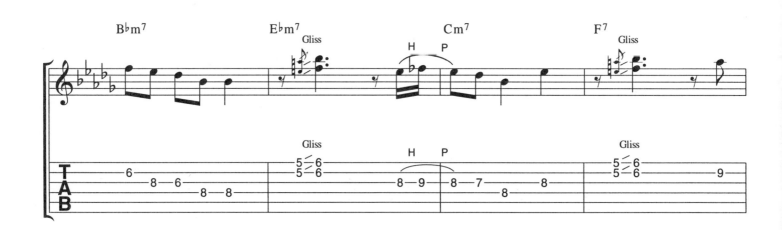

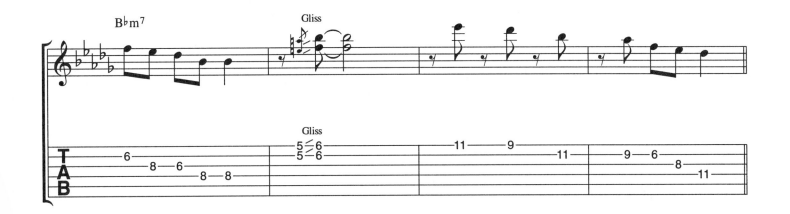

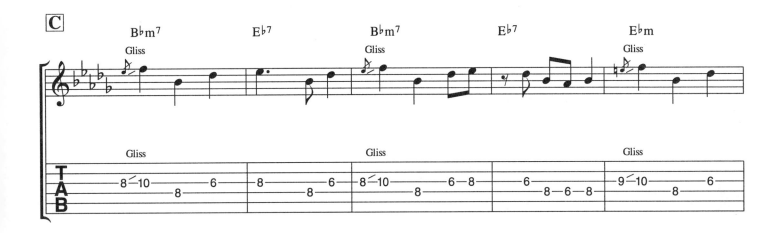

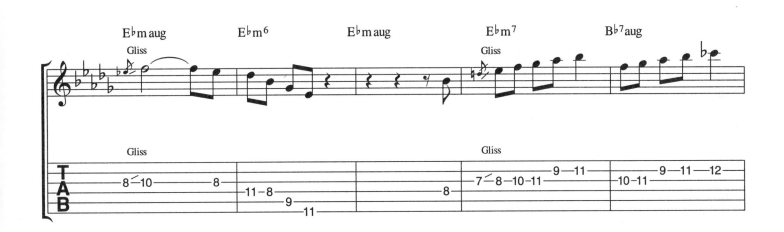

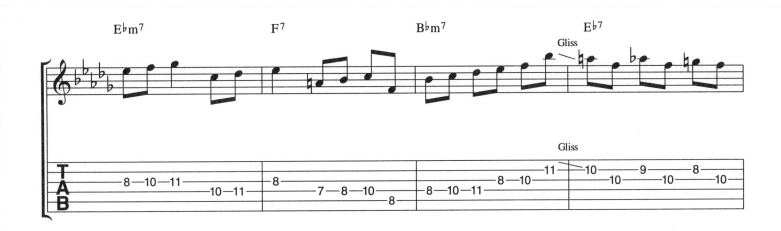

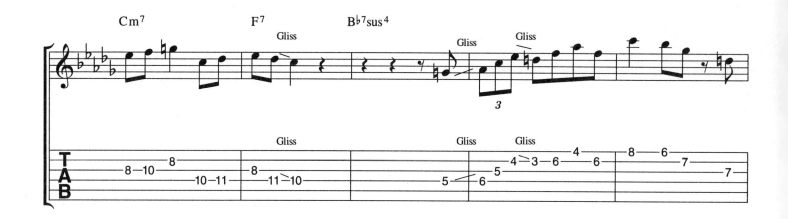

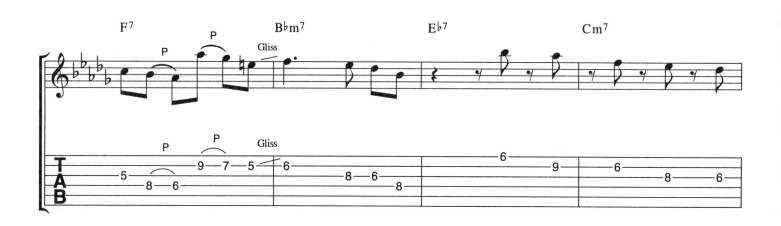

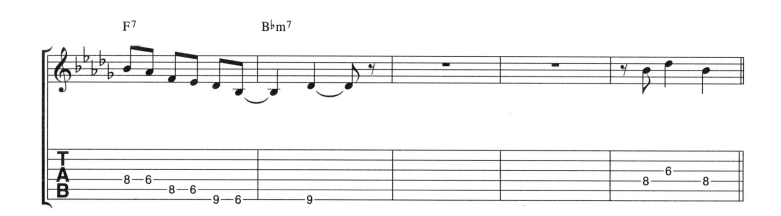

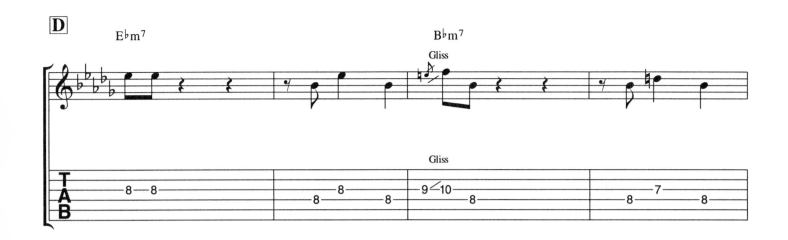

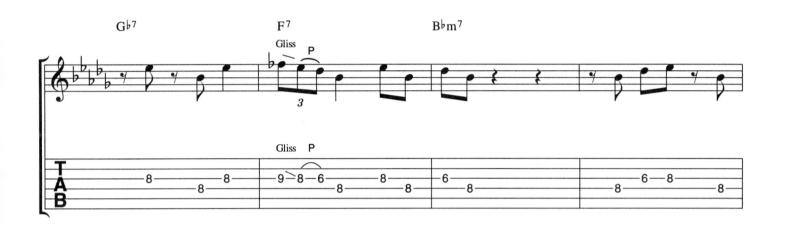

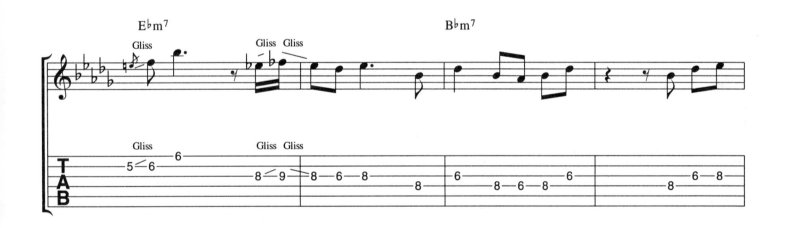

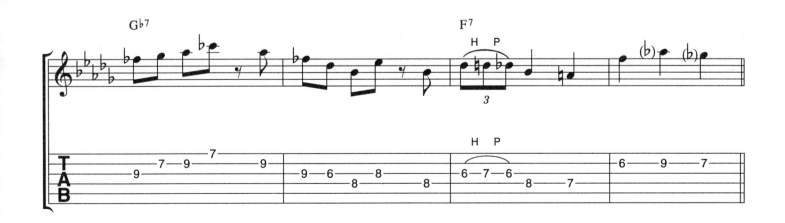

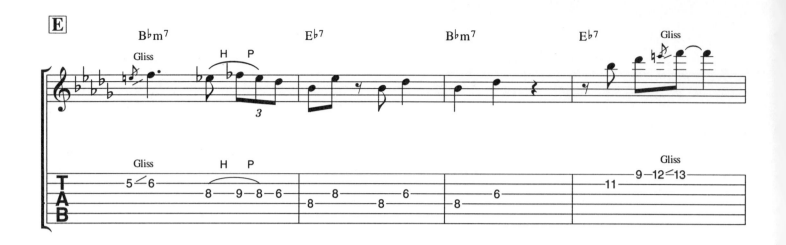

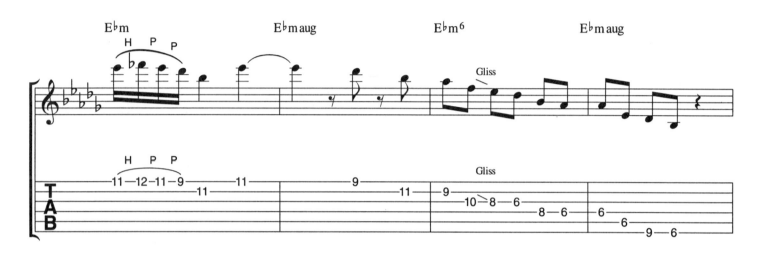

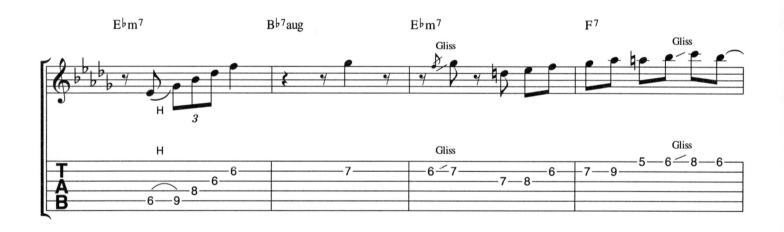

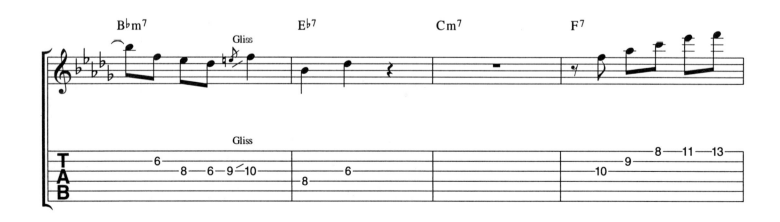

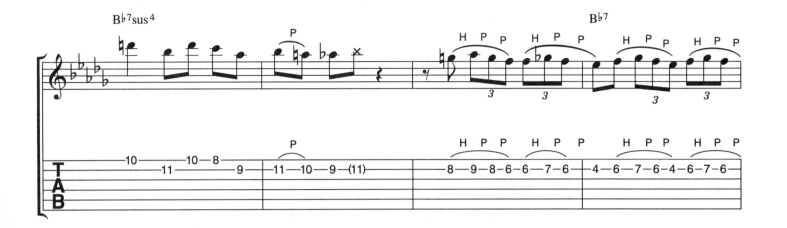

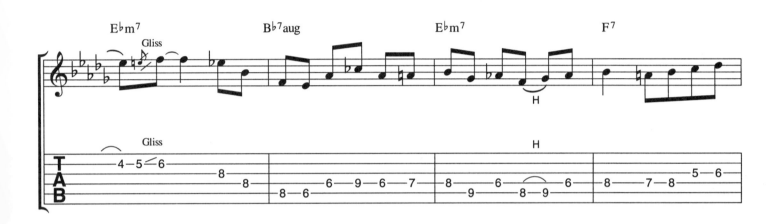

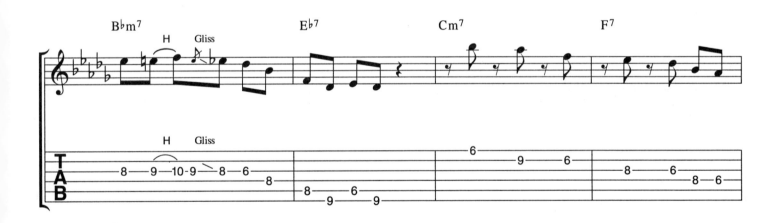

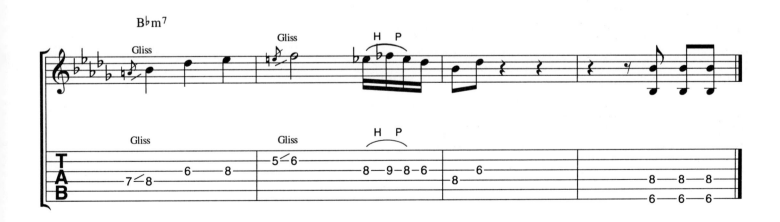

blue 'n' boogie

by john 'dizzy' gillespie & frank paparelli

Wes's solo on 'Blue 'n' Boogie' is a classic and would be well worth learning in its entirety. To get the most from this piece, however, take note of how Wes approaches the chords of this bebop blues. Isolate small segments of the solo and check out the tensions he uses against each of the chords. Consider the rhythms – the opening phrase of the solo is so perfect that it really grabs your attention! Wes ends the improvisation with his trademark octaves.

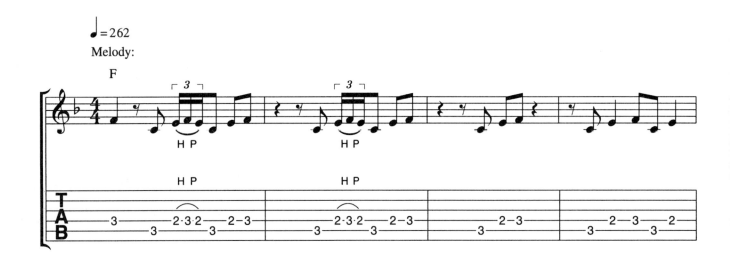

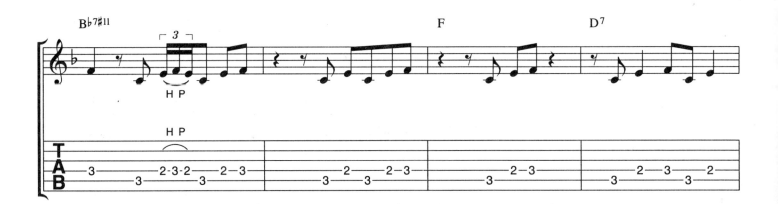

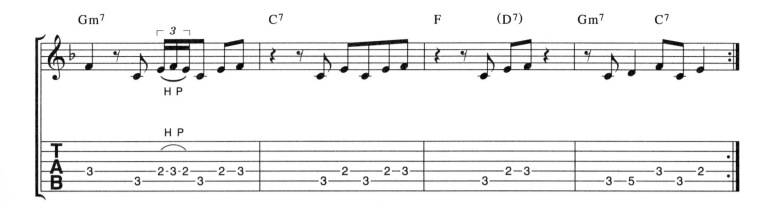

A Solo:

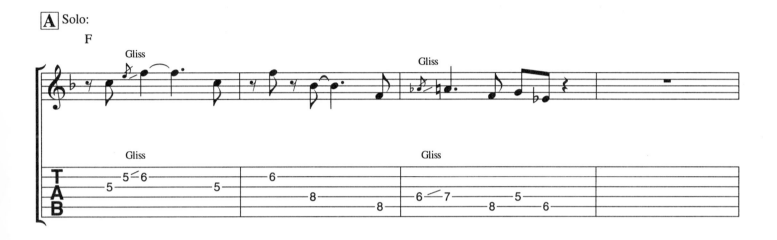

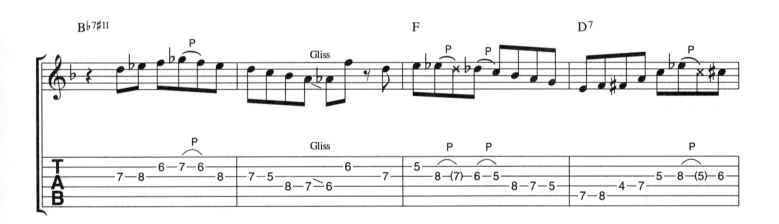

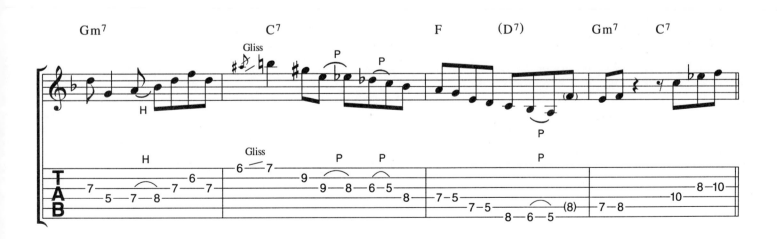

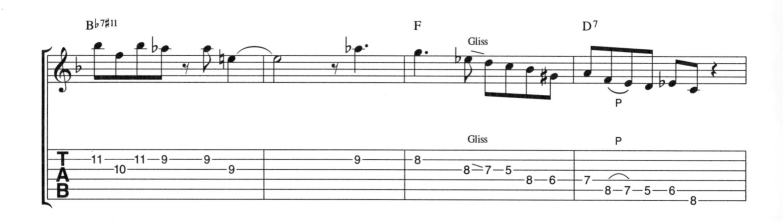

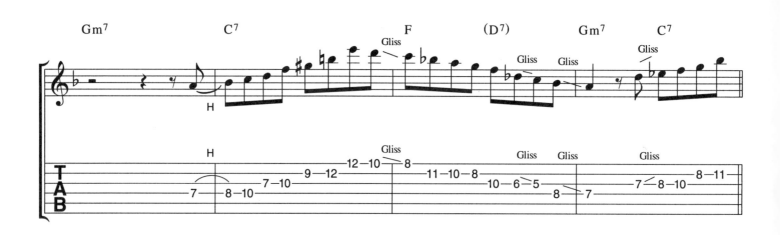

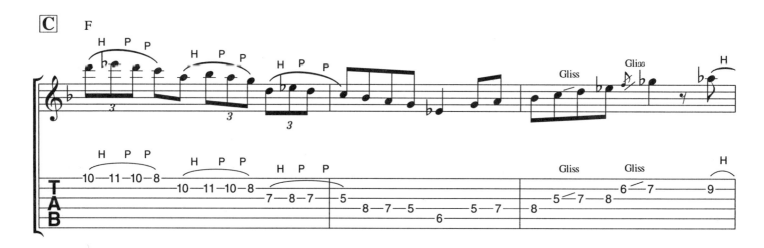

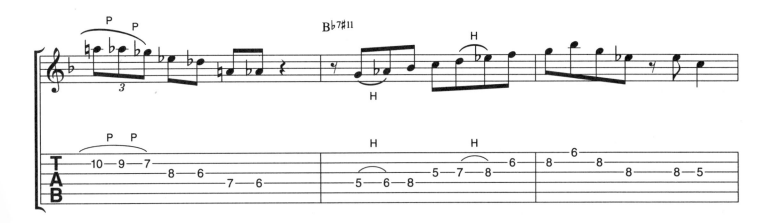

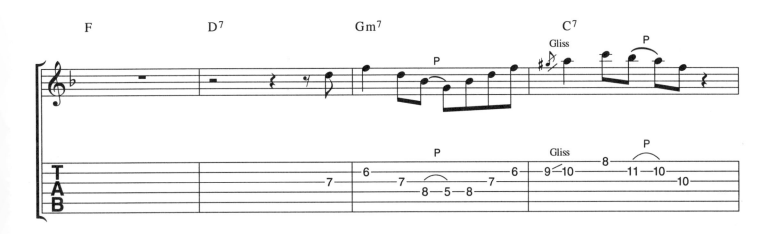

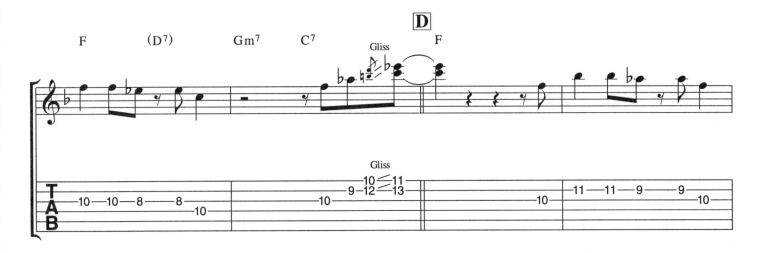

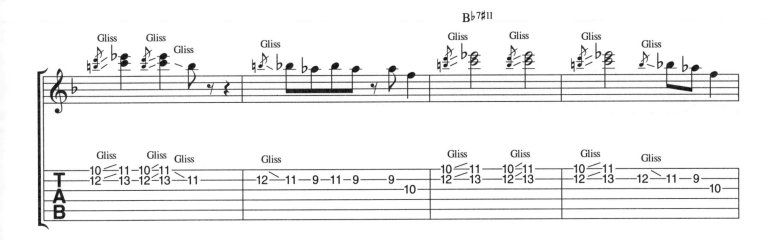

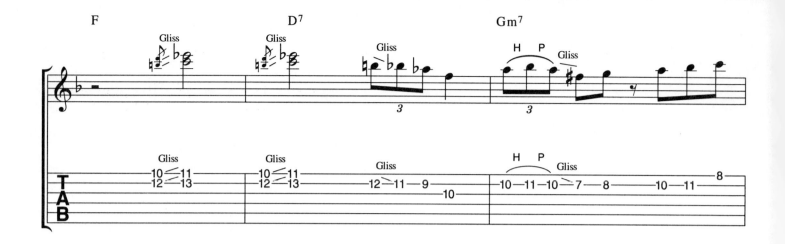

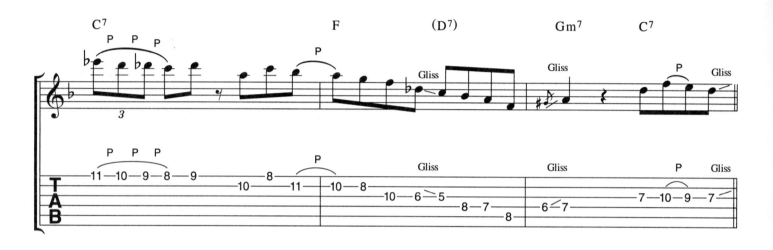

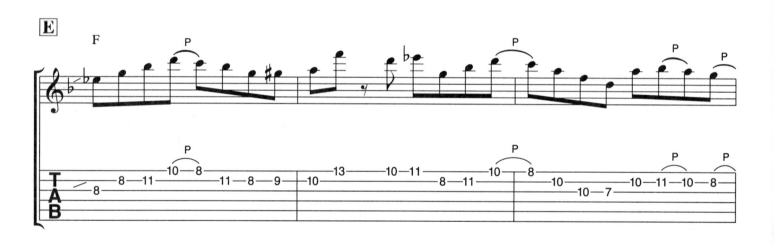

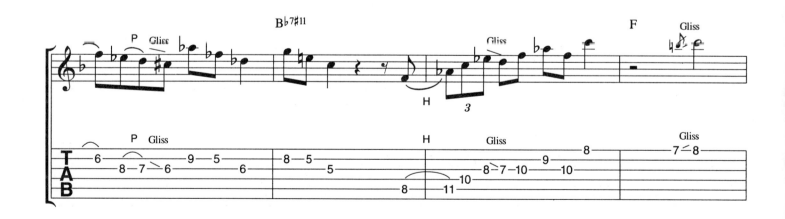

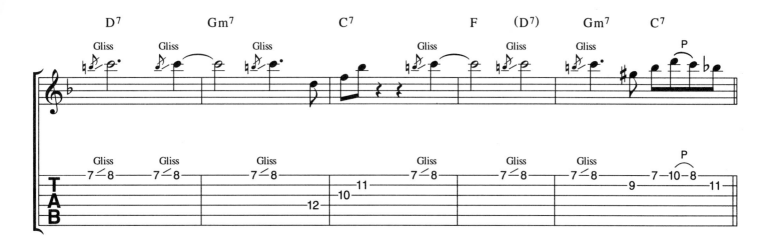

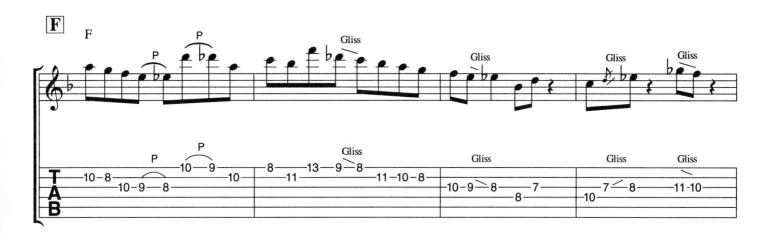

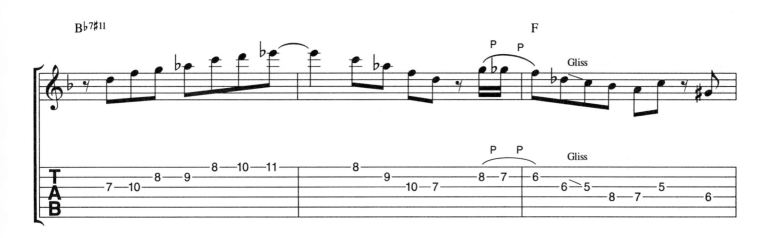

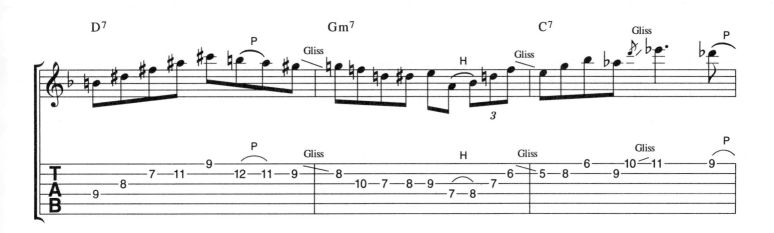

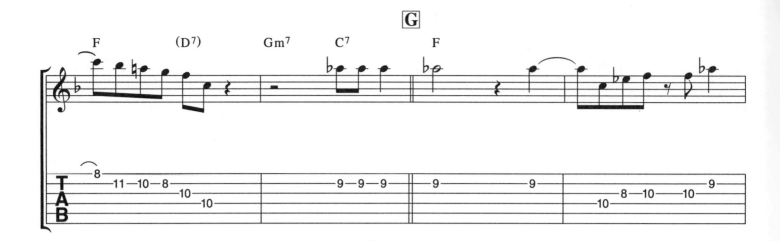

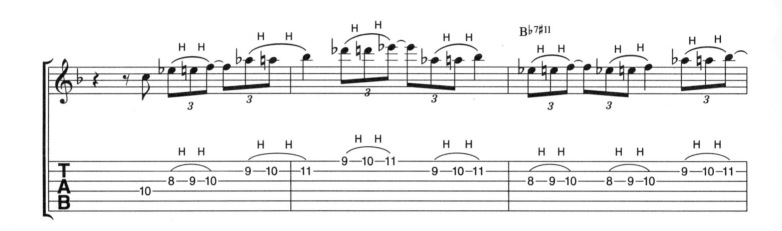

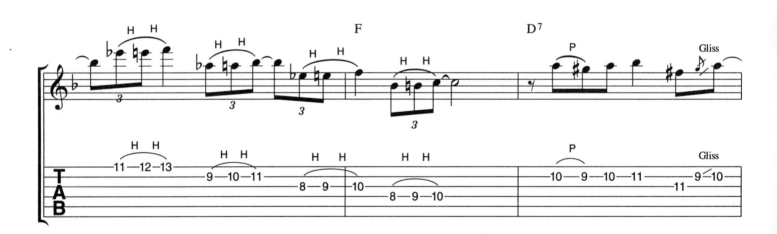

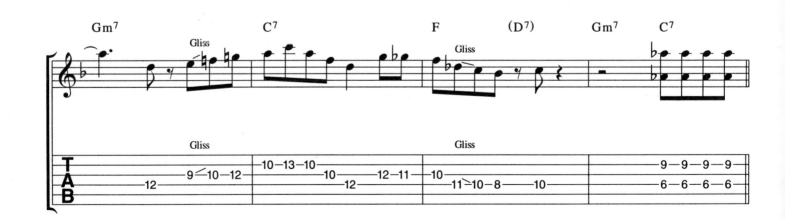

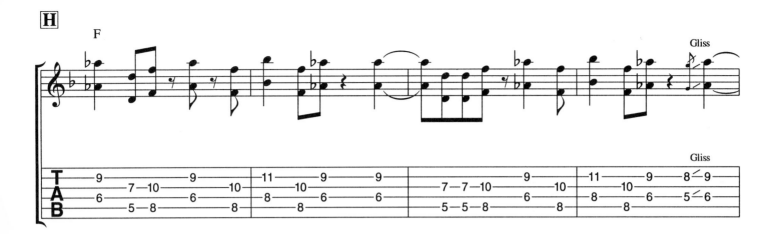

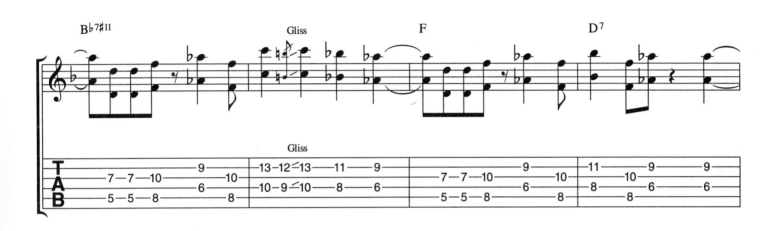

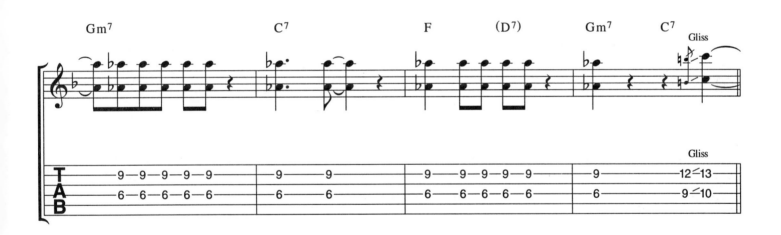

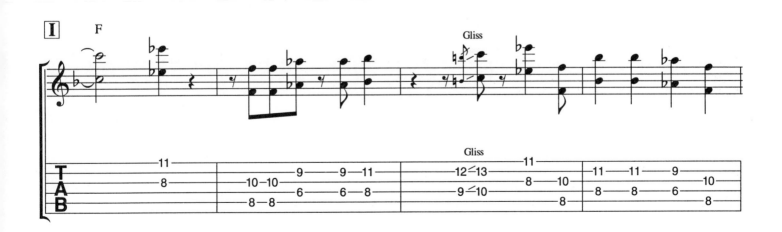

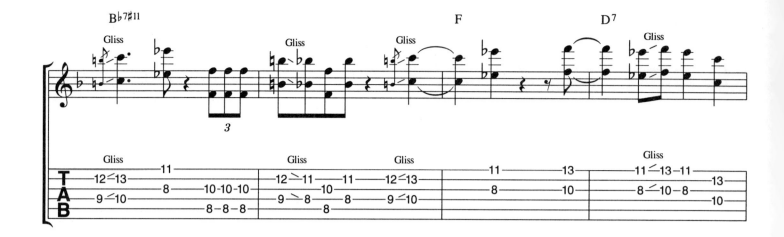

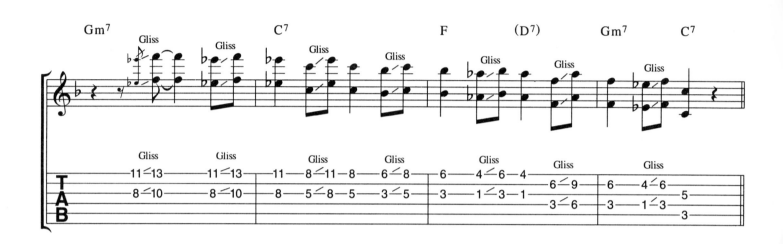

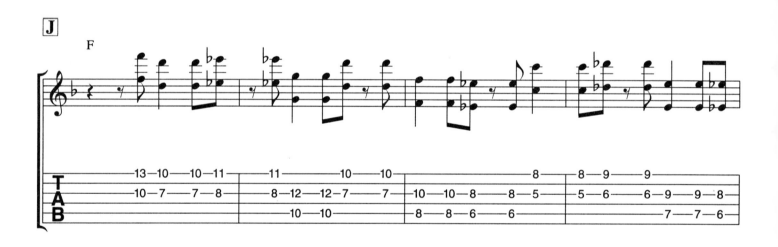

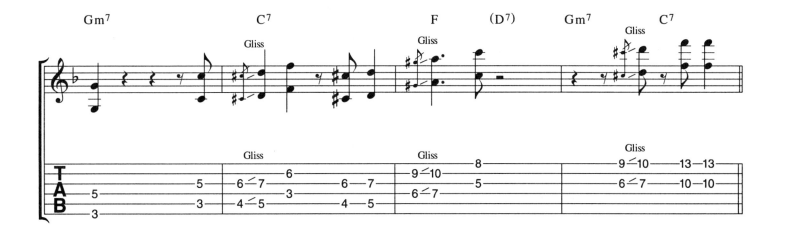

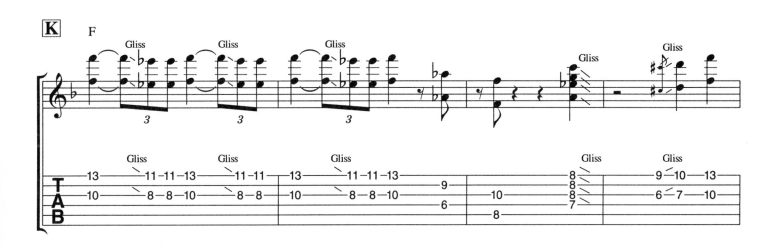

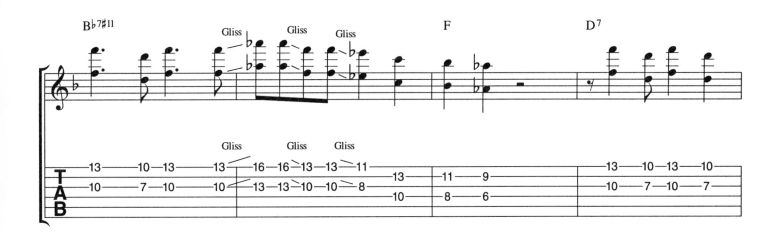

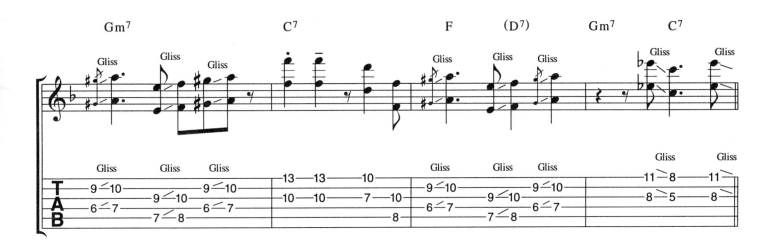

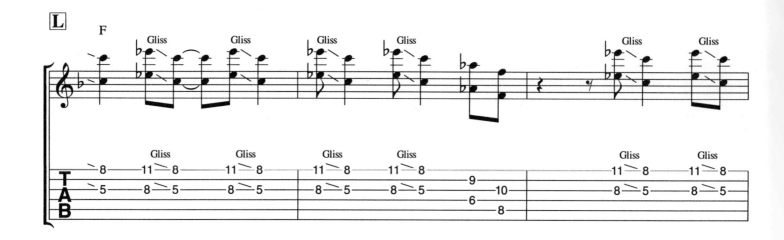

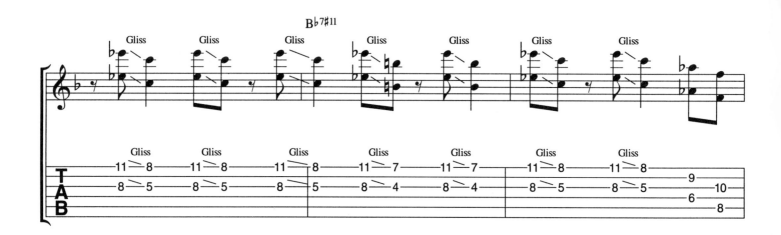

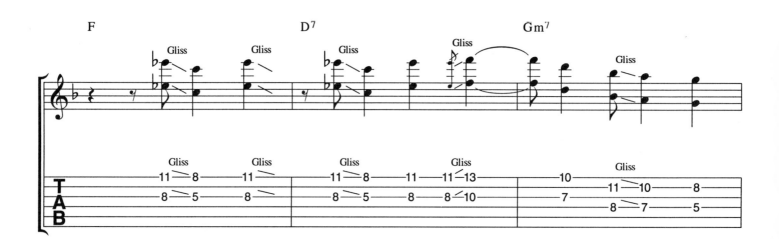

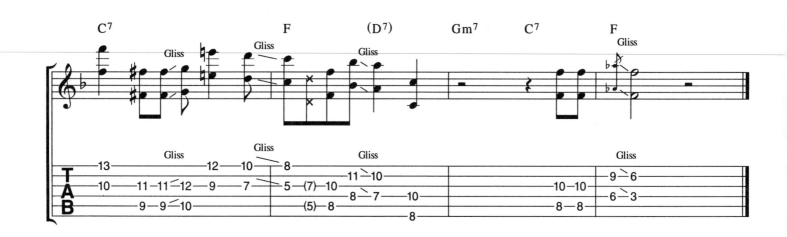

dearly beloved

music by jerome kern
words by johnny mercer

Wes really shows off his technique on this storming version of 'Dearly Beloved'. It's amazing to think that he could cut these fast tempos playing with his right hand thumb only. The arrangement of the tune is interesting for a number of reasons. The intro features triads over a tonic pedal. At the start of the solo we suddenly get the whole band playing a rhythmic unison figure on the chord of D7sus4. Note that Wes often uses E♭m7 – A♭7 instead of D7. This is a commmon jazz device – the flat 5 substitution. The solo itself is a mixture of simple repetitive ideas and hip bebop eighth-note lines. Practise these extended lines slowly, especially if the shapes are unfamiliar. Wes also plays a number of lines here that are just quarter notes (crotchets). John Coltrane used to do this in order to help the whole band lock into the pulse.

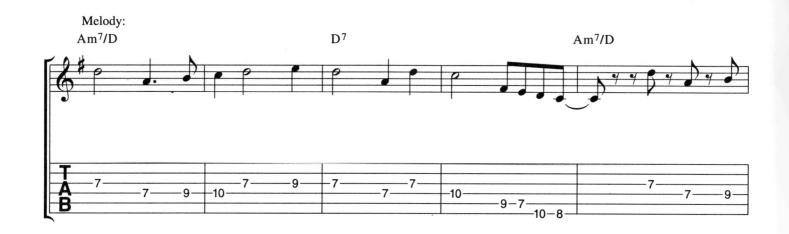

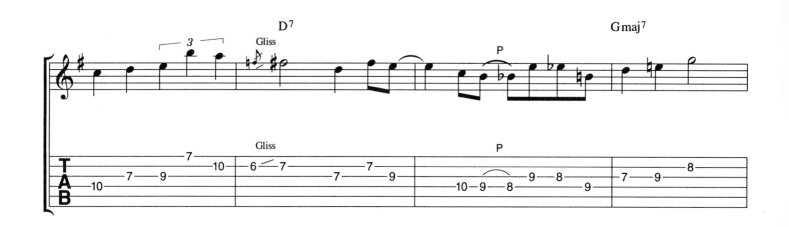

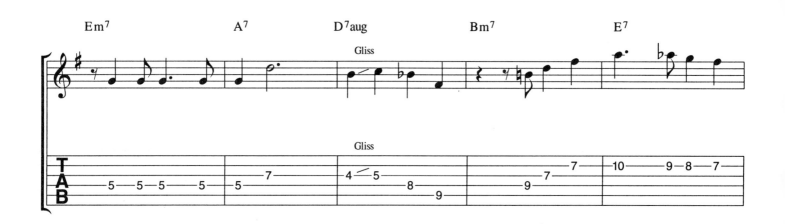

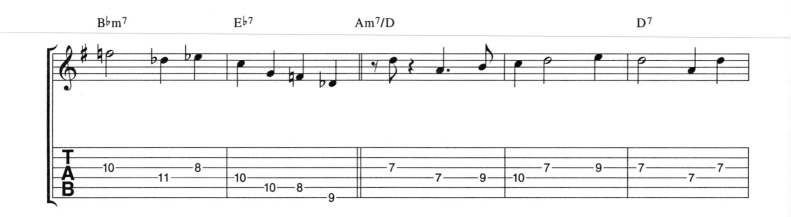

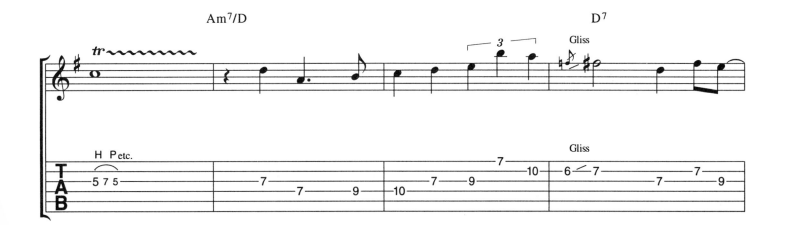

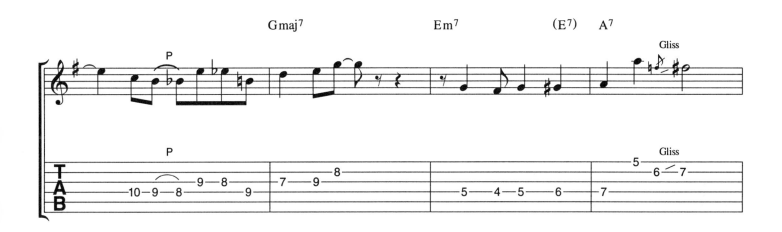

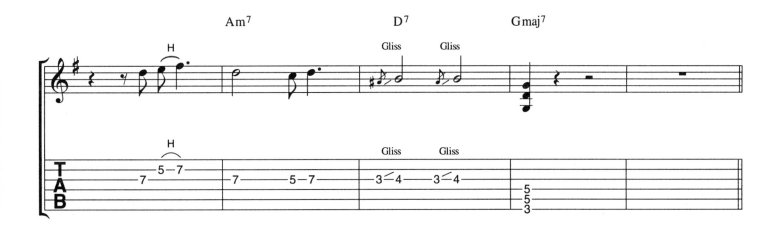

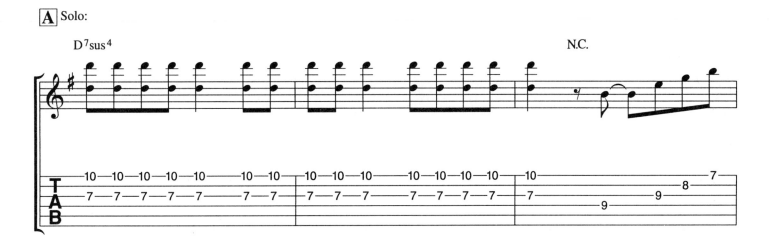

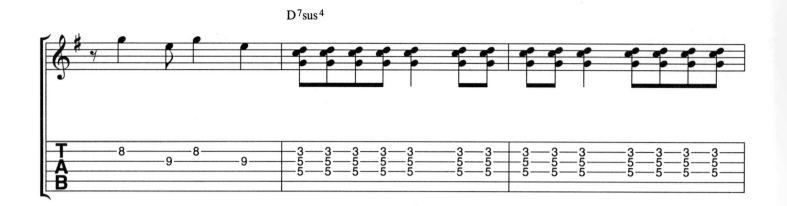

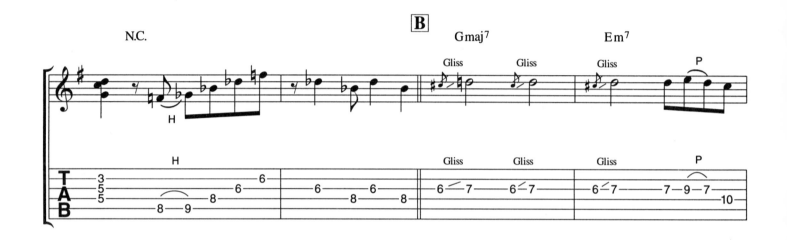

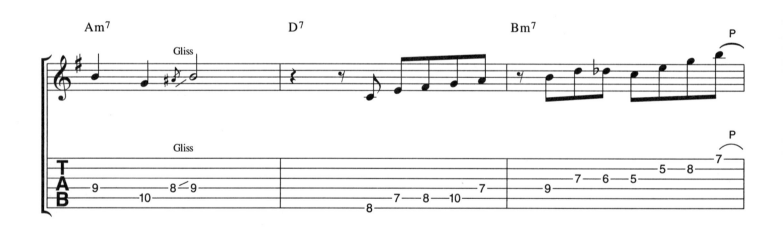

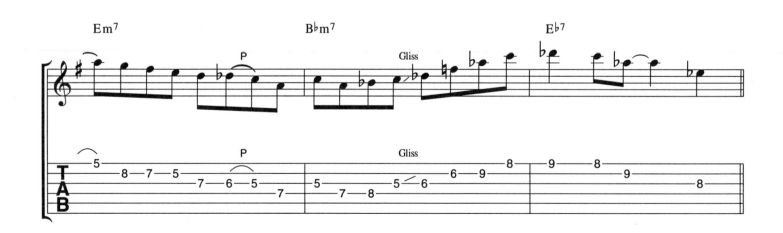

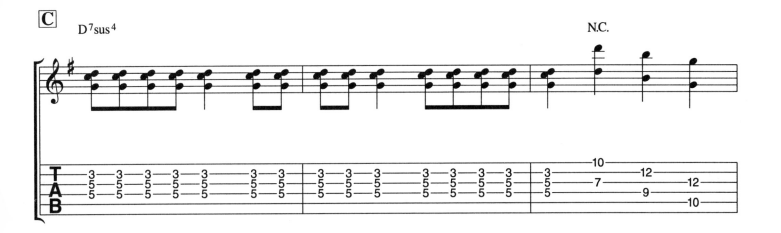

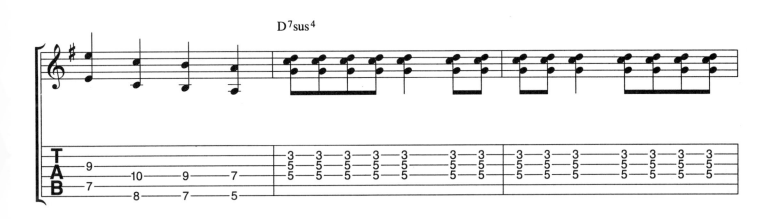

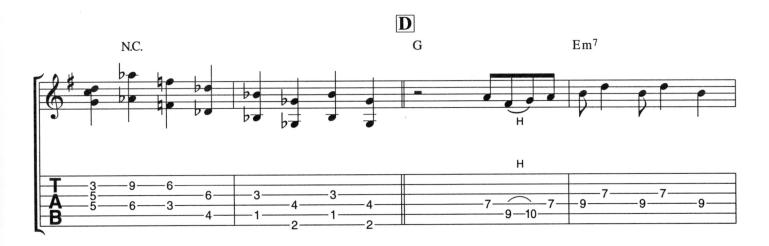

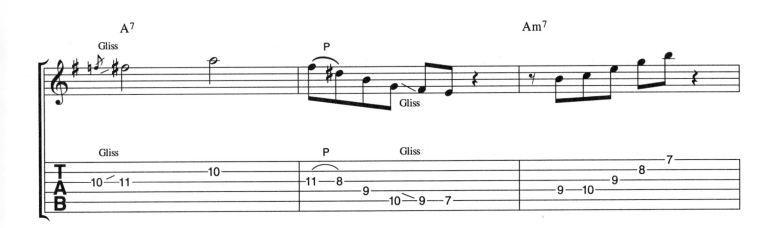

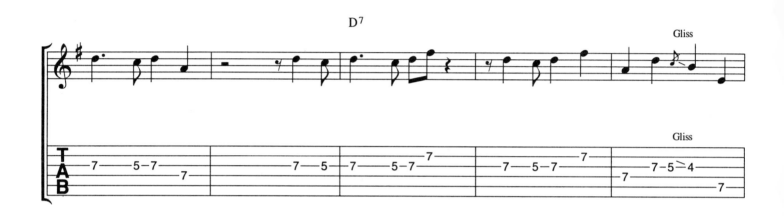

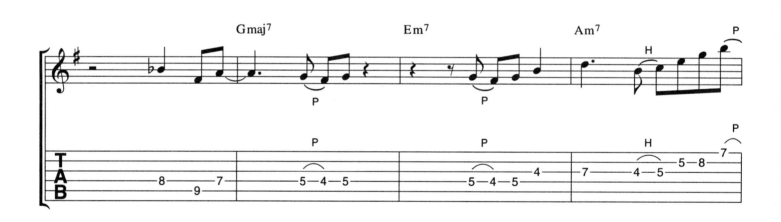

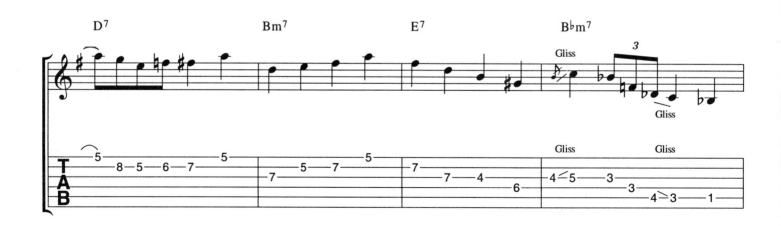

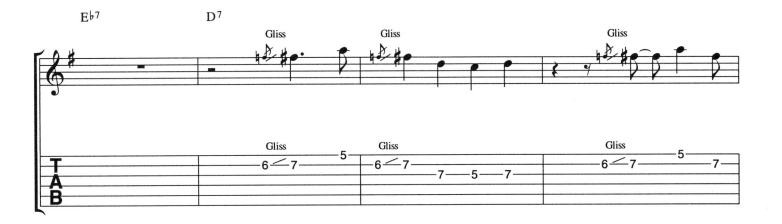

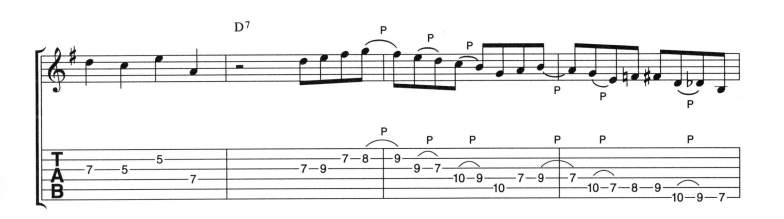

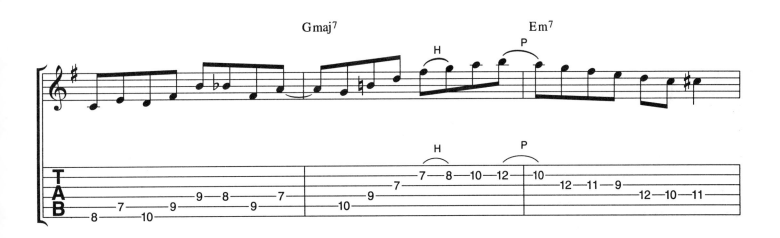

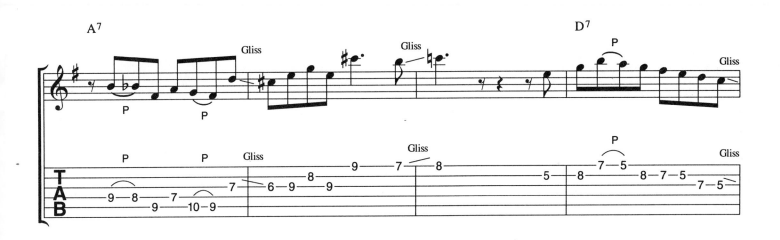

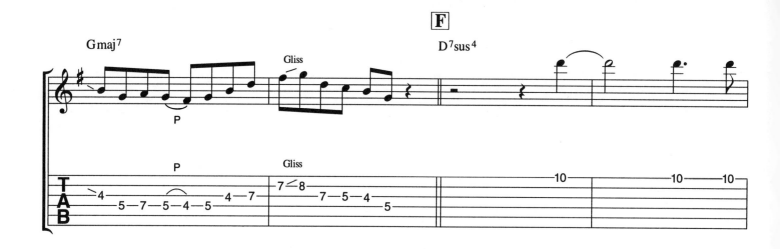

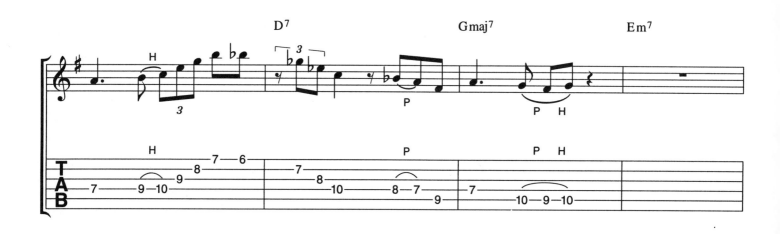

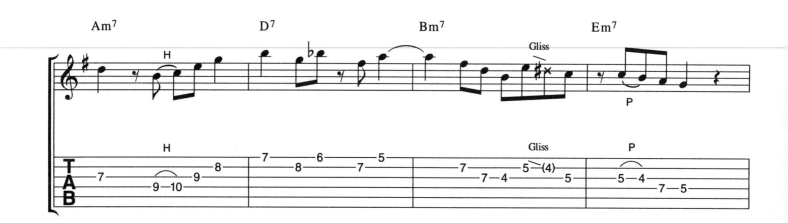

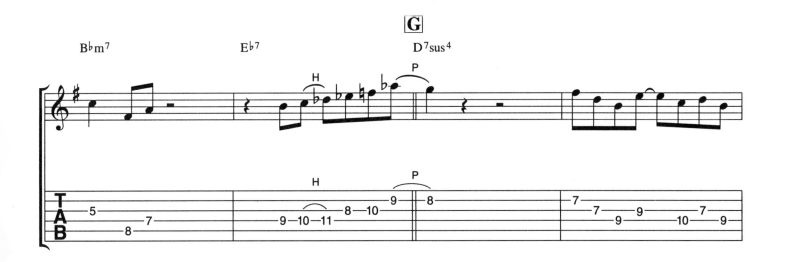

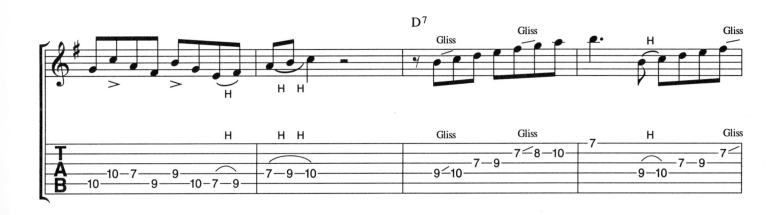

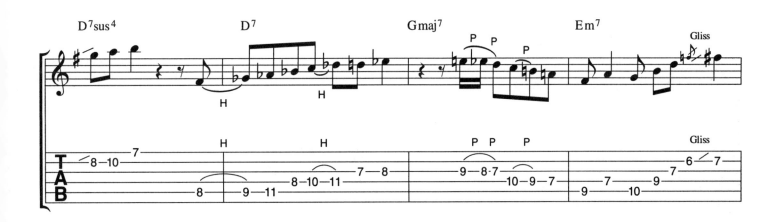

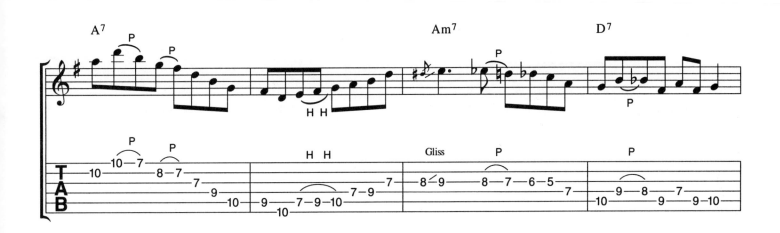

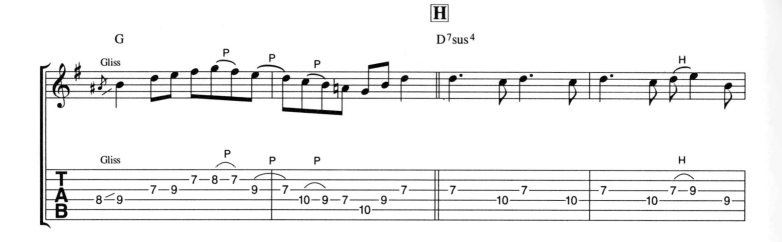

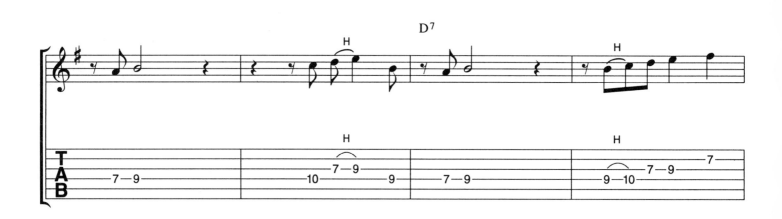

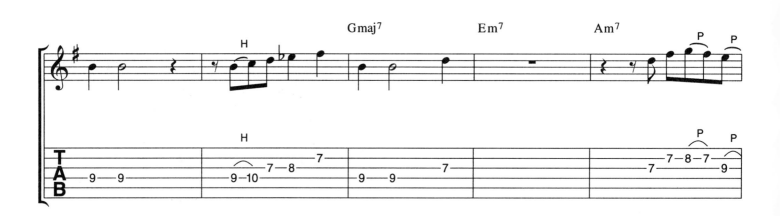

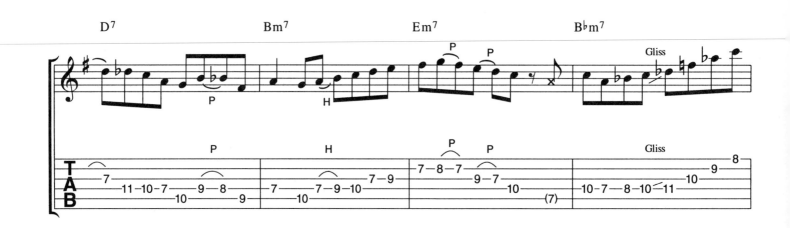

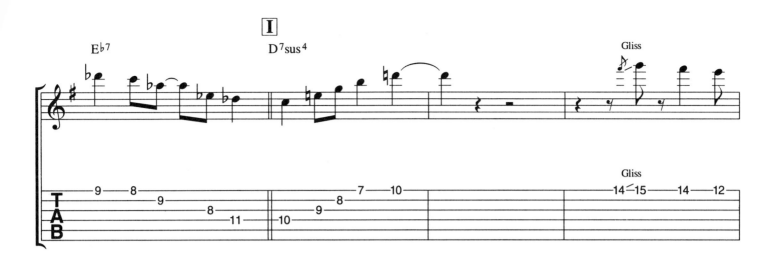

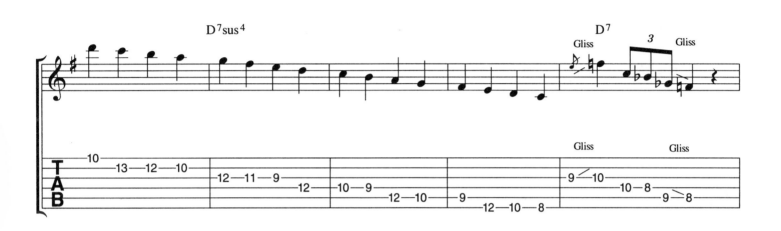

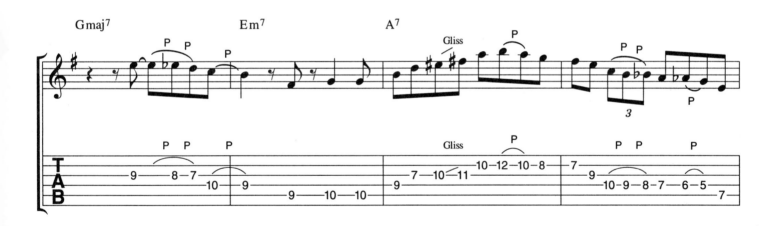

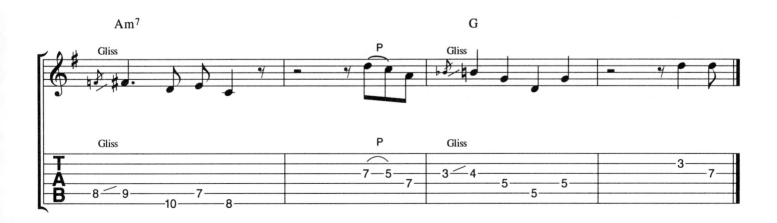

golden earrings

music by victor young
words by jay livingston & ray evans

This version of 'Golden Earrings' sees Wes playing with a big band. After a classical introduction by the woodwind section Wes plays the melody in octaves. He treats it in a stately manner, with interjections from the horn section and the cor anglais taking the middle section. When the improvisation comes, notice that we go to double-time swing tempo. Wes continues the octaves and plays a great bluesy solo.

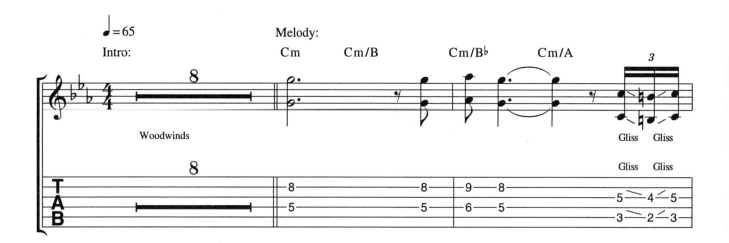

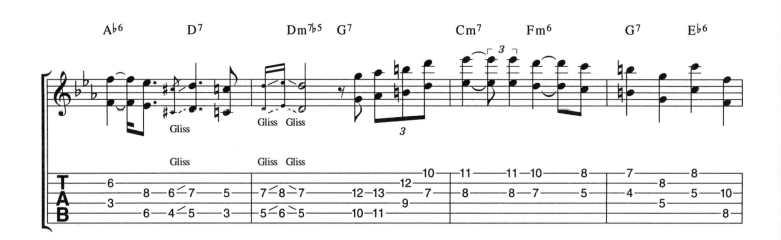

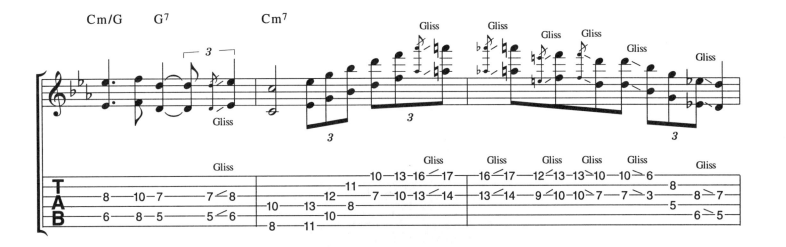

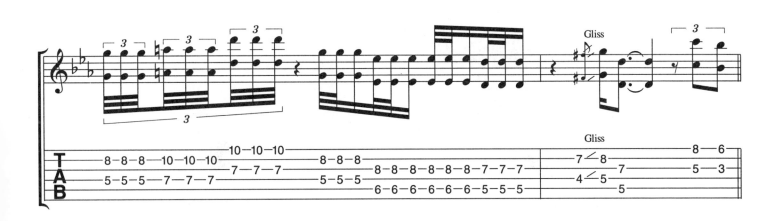

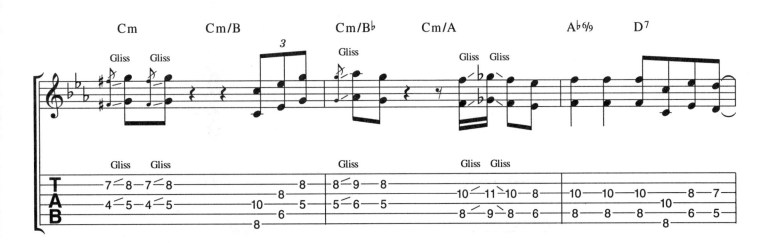

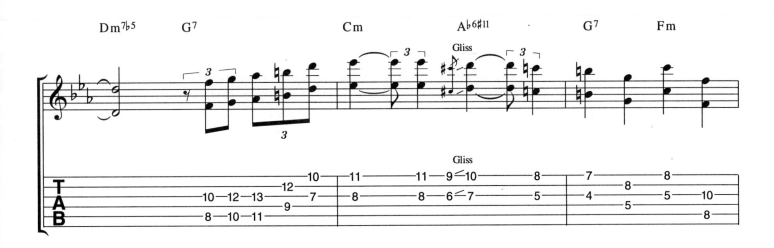

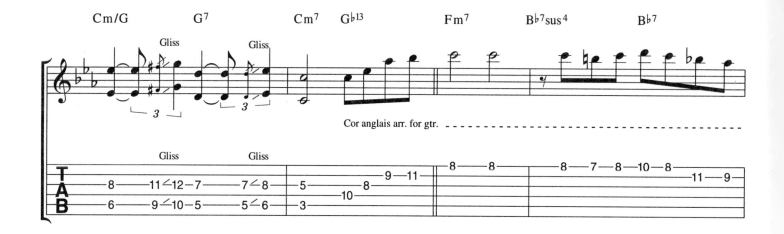

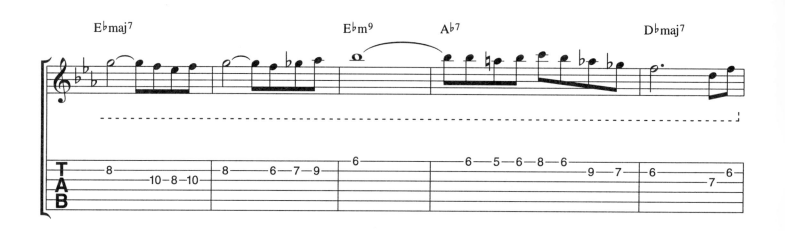

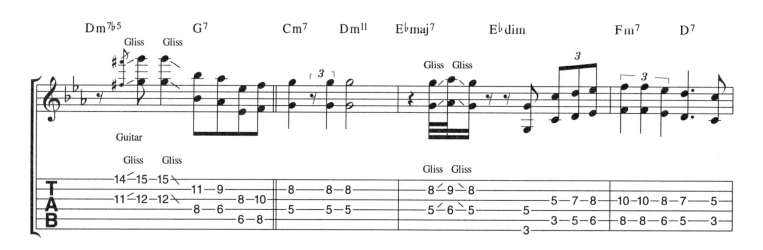

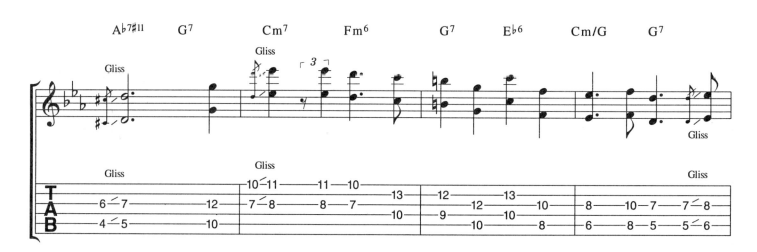

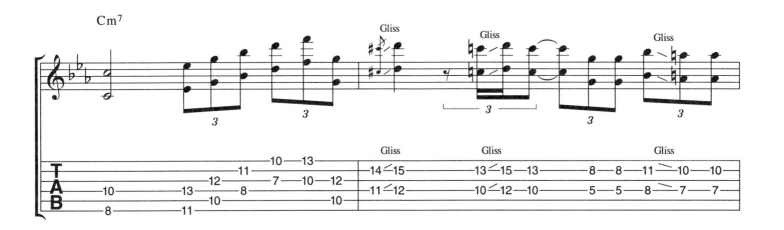

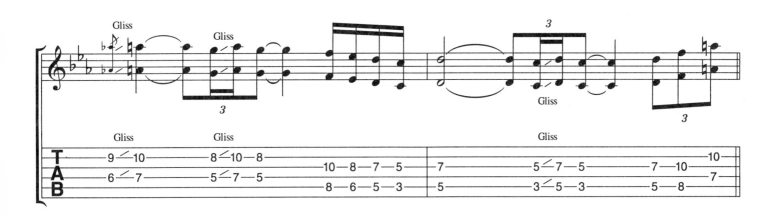

A Solo:

Double time ♩=♩

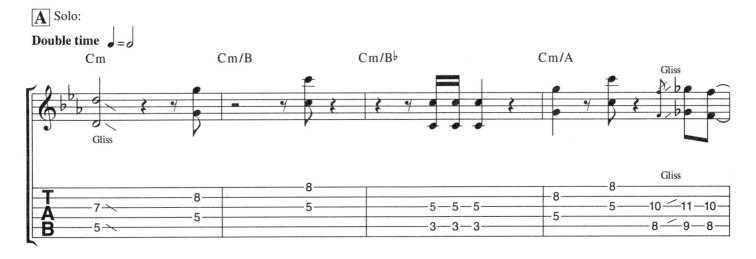

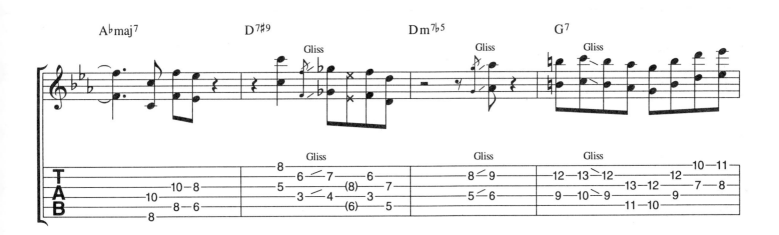

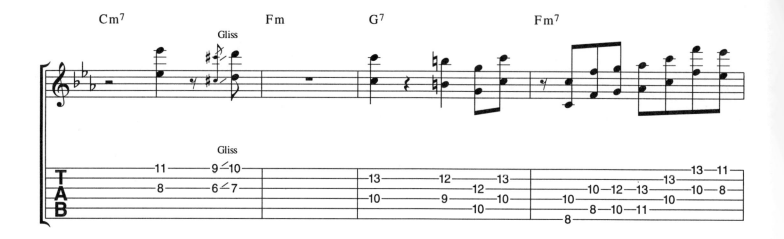

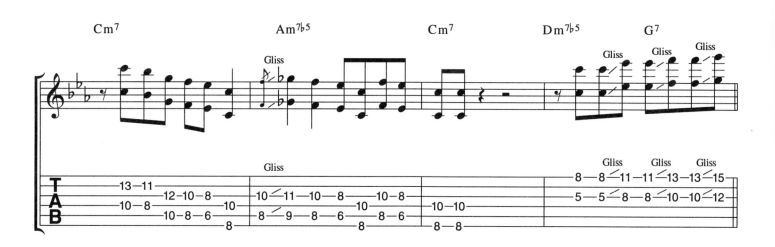

B

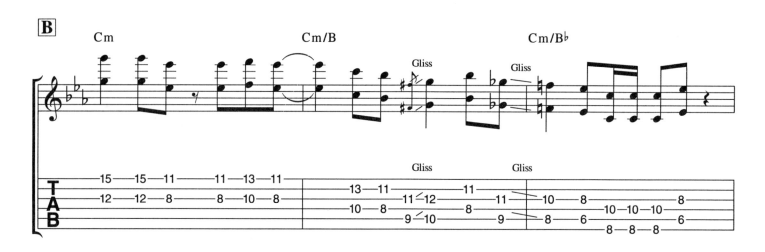

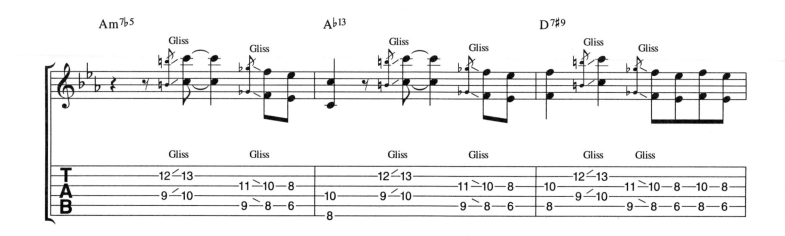

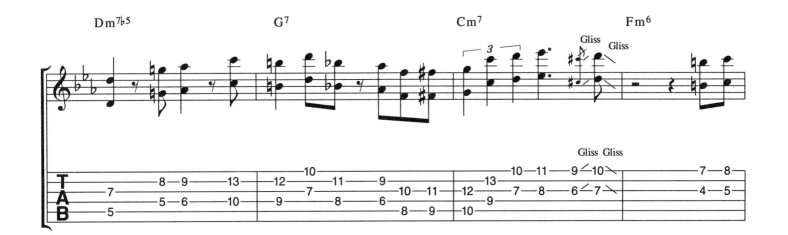

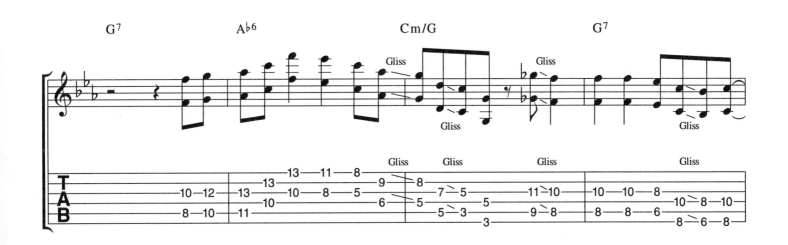

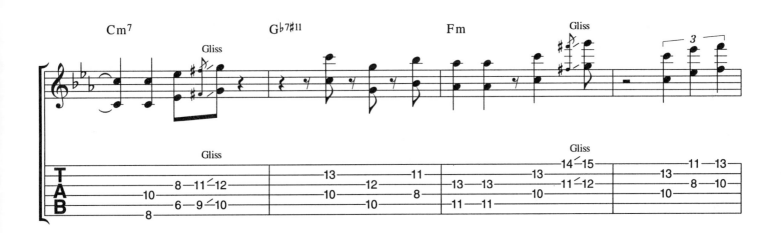

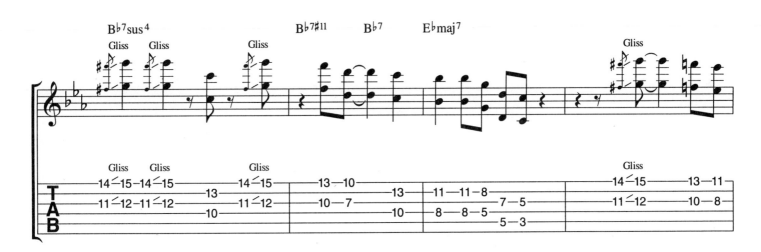

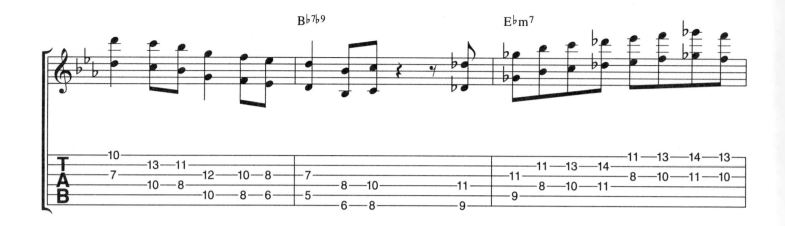

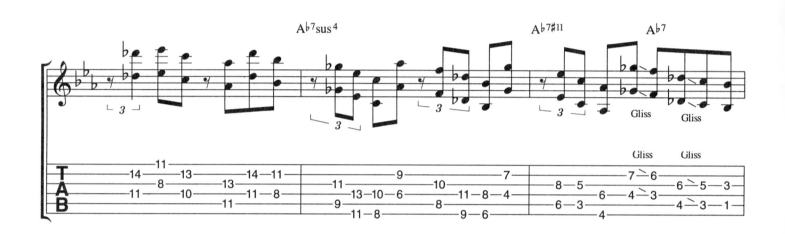

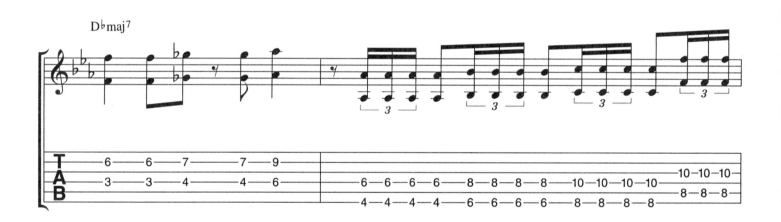

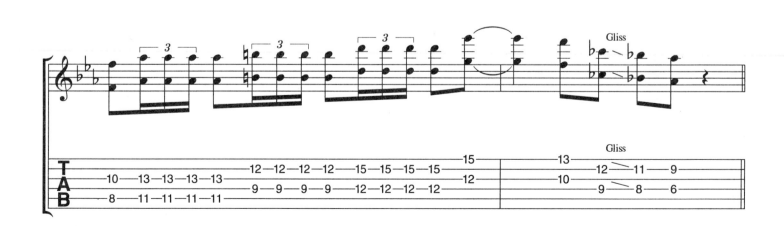

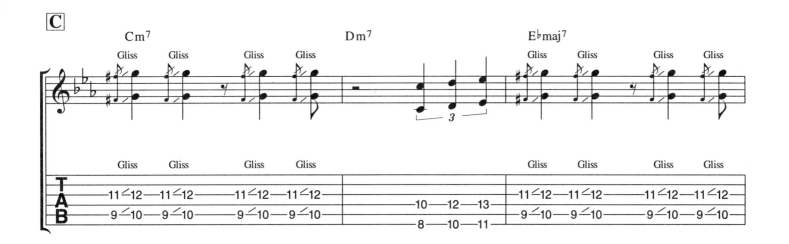

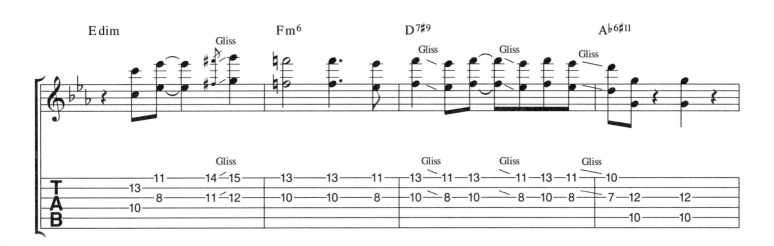

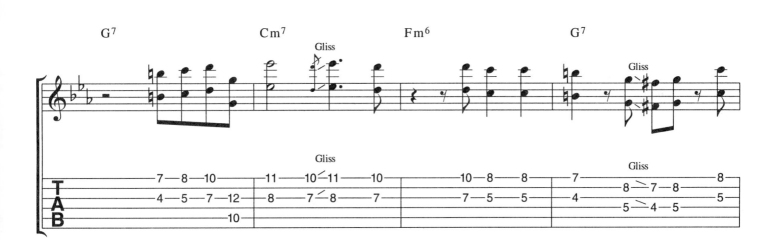

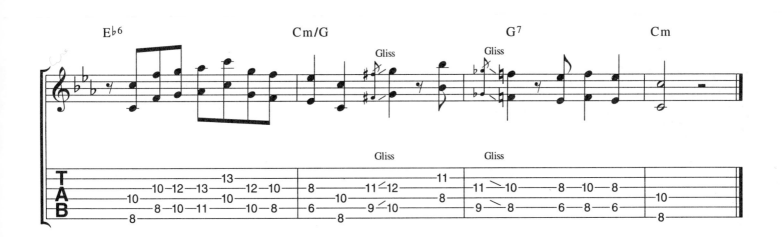

in your own sweet way

music by dave brubeck
words by iola brubeck

After a beautiful piano intro by Tommy Flanagan, Wes delivers the melody of 'In Your Own Sweet Way' in chord form. Again, the voicings and alterations to the chords are well worth investigating. Tommy Flanagan plays the middle eight in a florid style. It's very important that we listen to the way these great players ornament a melody. Flanagan fills up the gaps and creates shapes around the original tune. Wes's solo is a masterpiece of ballad playing. It's jam-packed with strong ideas and unfolds beautifully. Wes always seems to come up with a knockout opening statement in a solo.

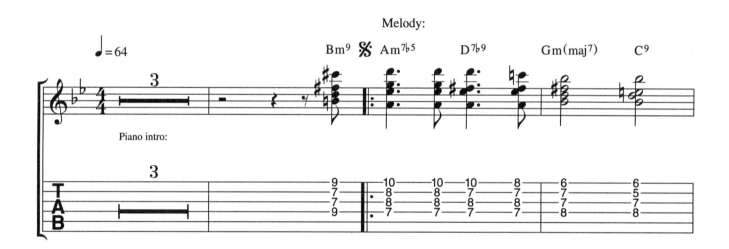

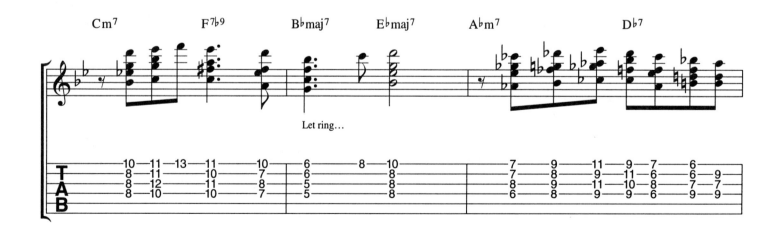

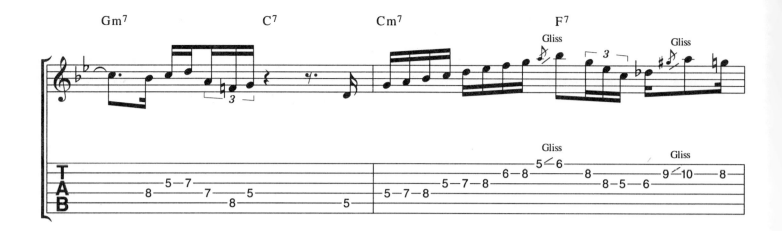

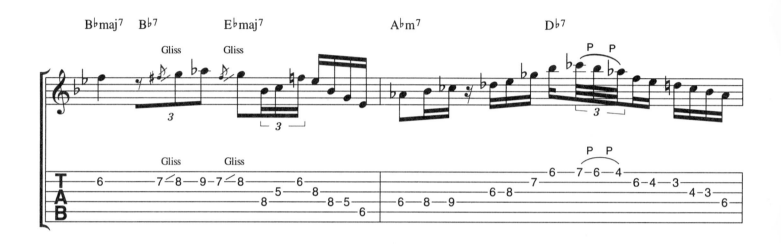

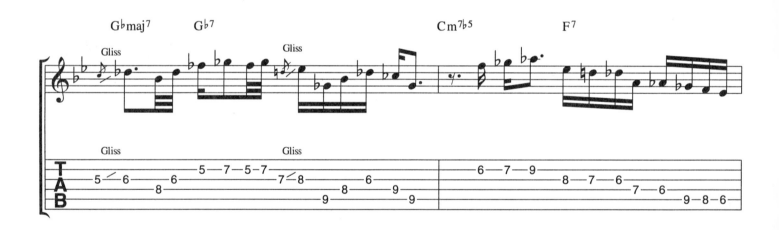

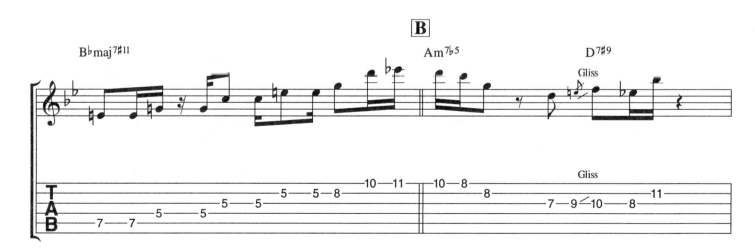

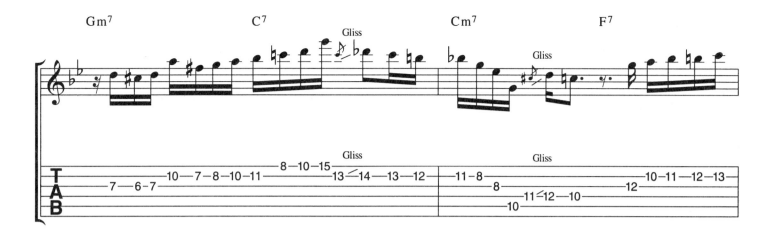

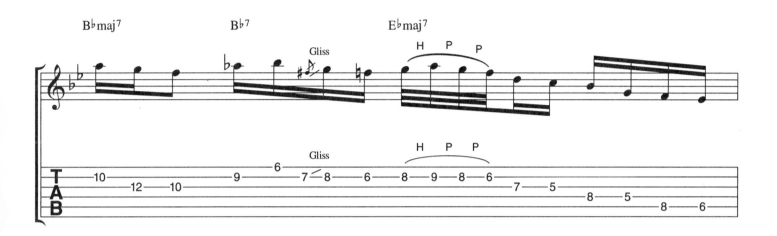

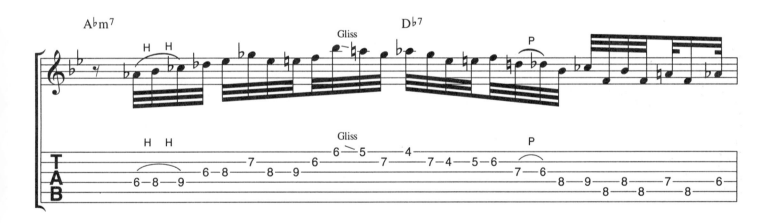

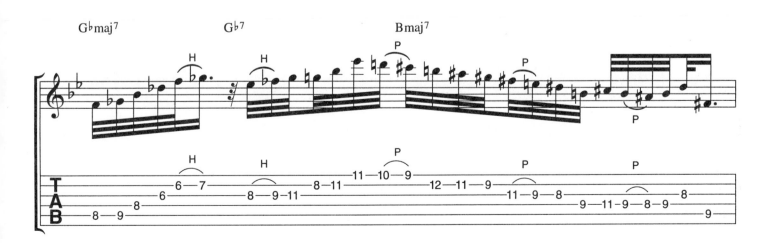

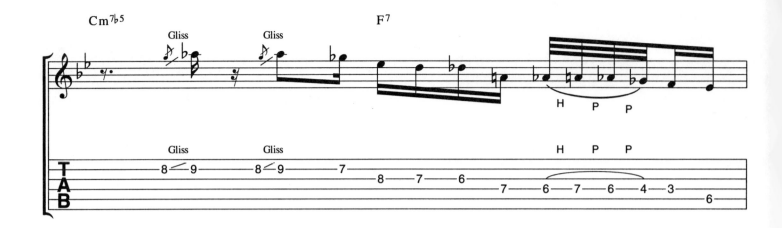

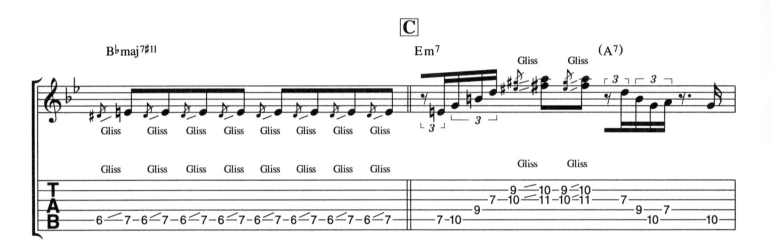

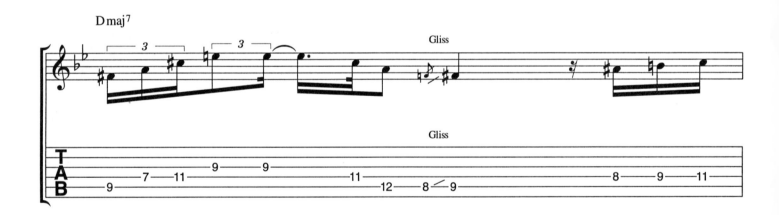

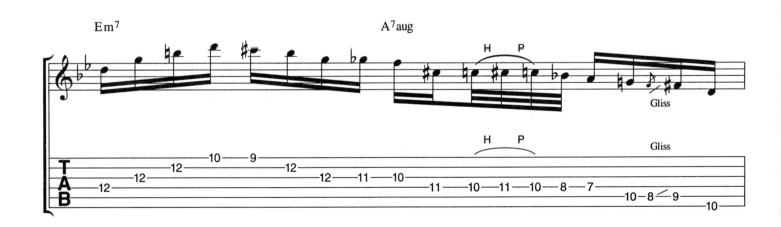

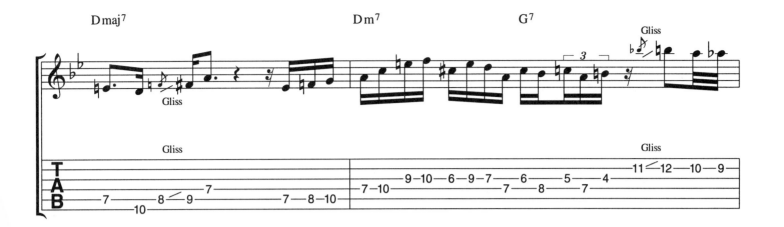

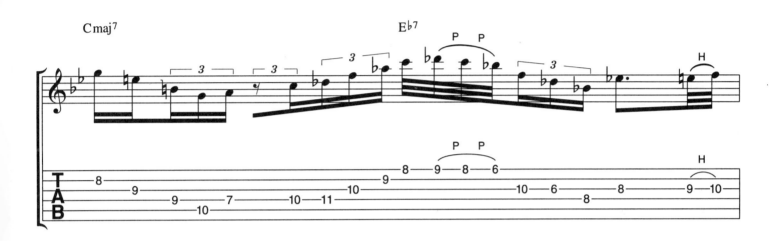

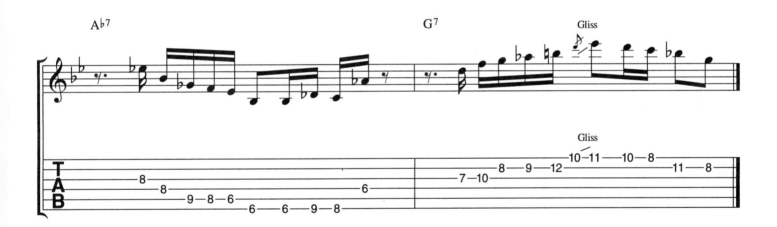

satin doll

words by johnny mercer
music by duke ellington & billy strayhorn

On this tune Wes plays the melody alongside the organ of Mel Rhyne. Wes is actually not playing the melody line at the top of his voicings at the start of the tune. He's playing what would naturally be the next note down in the voicing. The chord voicings used in this piece are well worth a look. They're often close to the standard shapes, but you'll find interesting altered notes and spacings between the tones. The solo opens with Wes working the first bar as a theme for development. There is a wealth of jazz vocabulary in this short solo. Play the recording repeatedly and try to learn the solo well enough to be able to sing along with it. Singing is the best way to internalise the phrasing of the jazz masters. Also try playing the solo – or even just a fragment of it – along with the recording. This will help you to get a sense of swing.

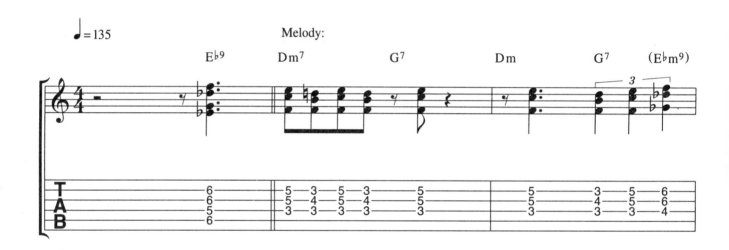

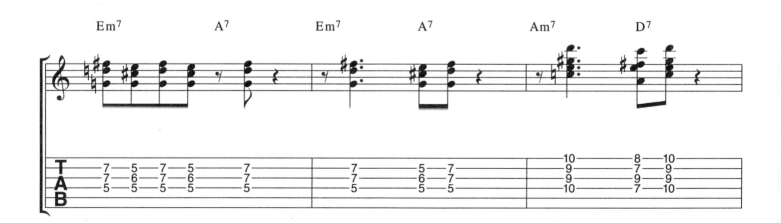

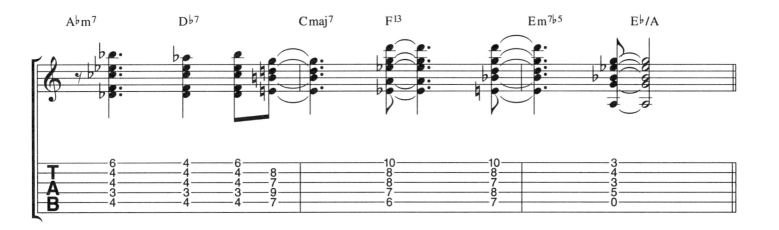

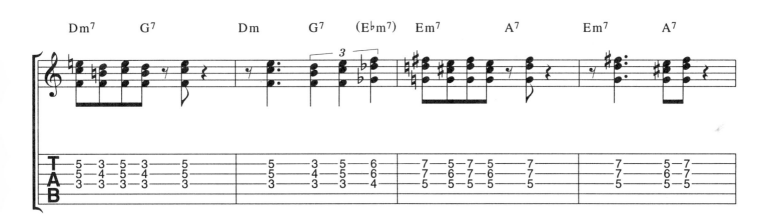

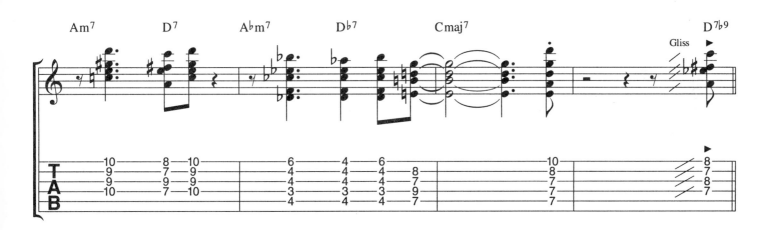

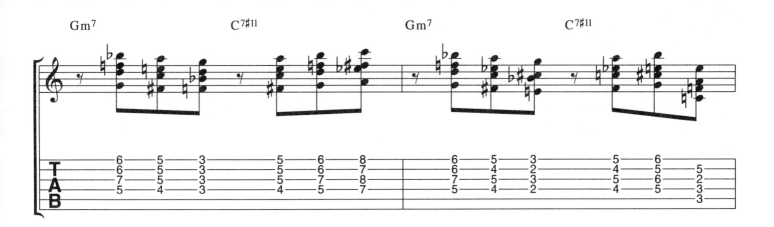

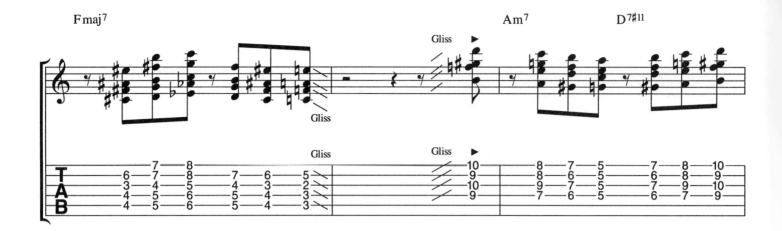

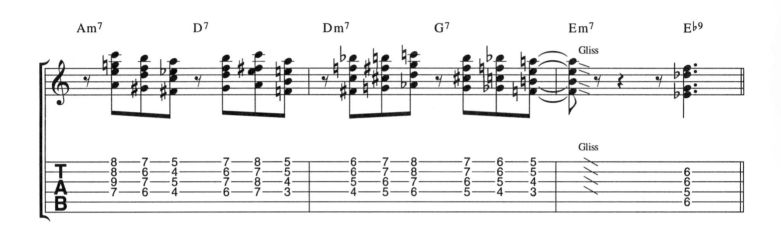

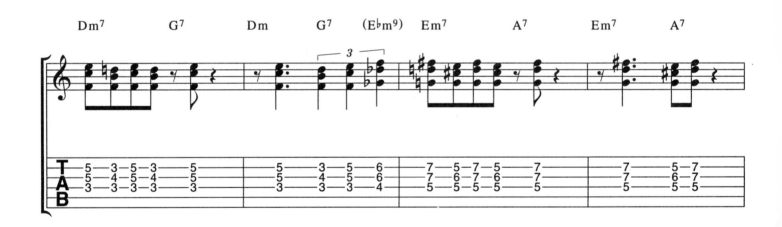

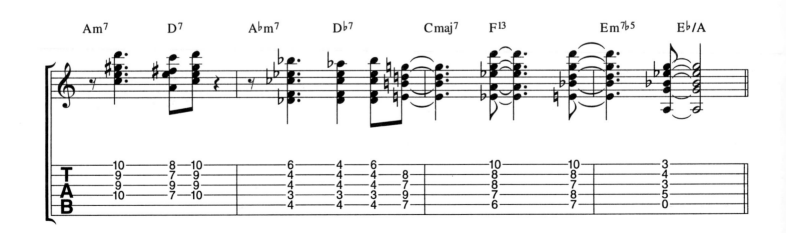

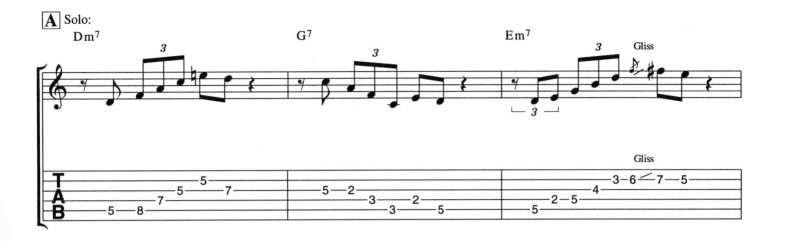

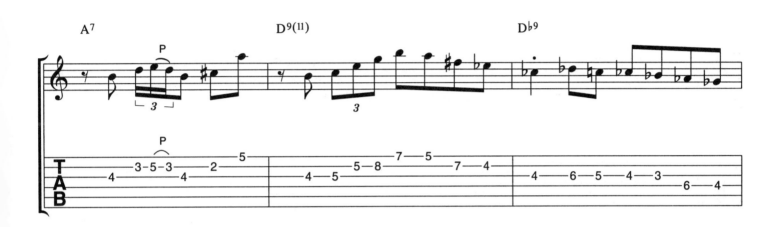

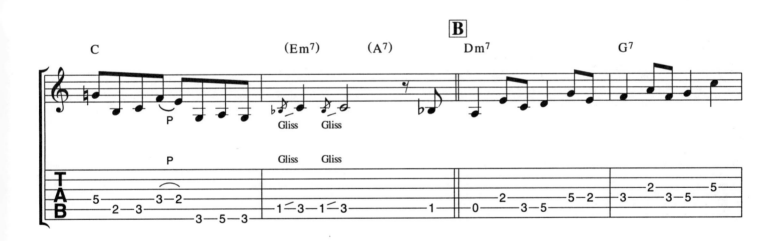

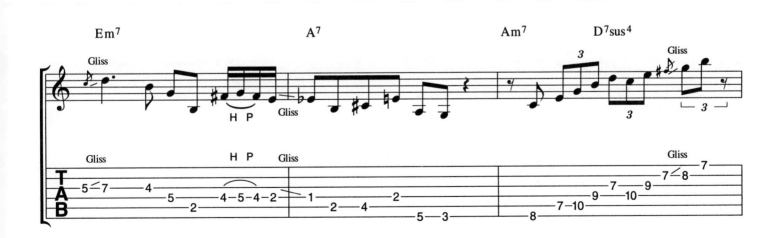

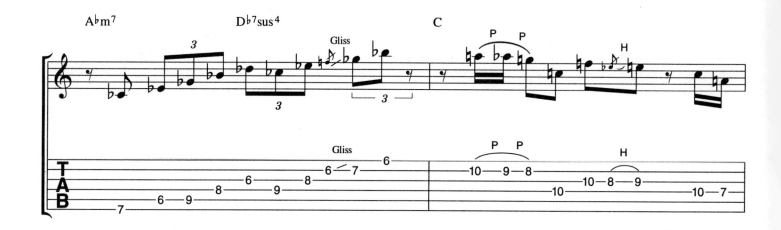

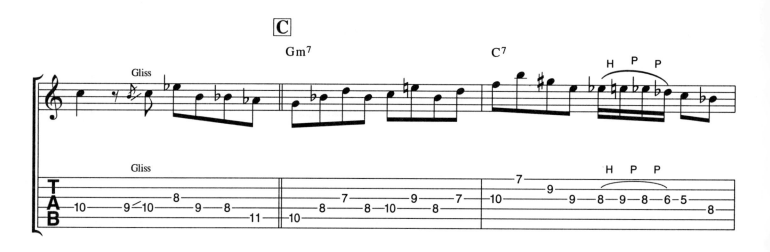

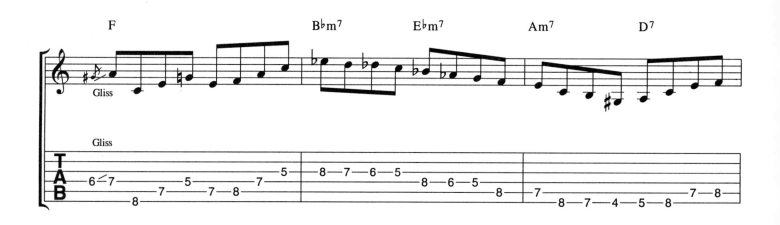

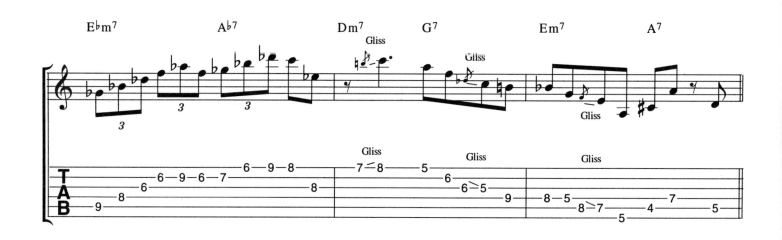

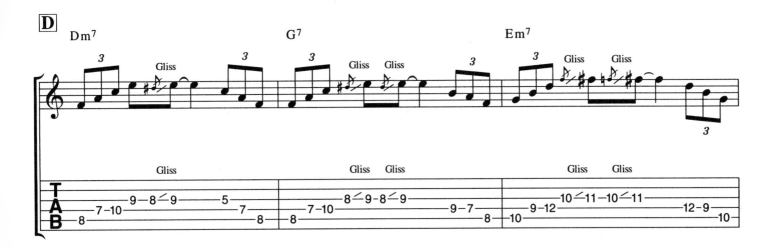

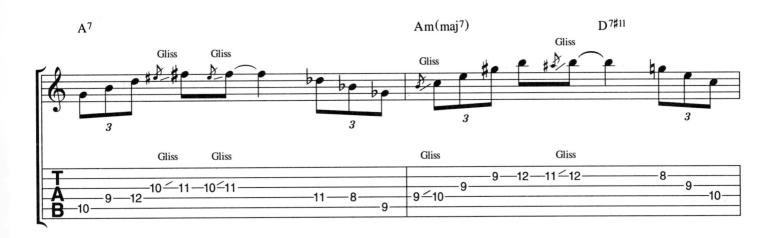

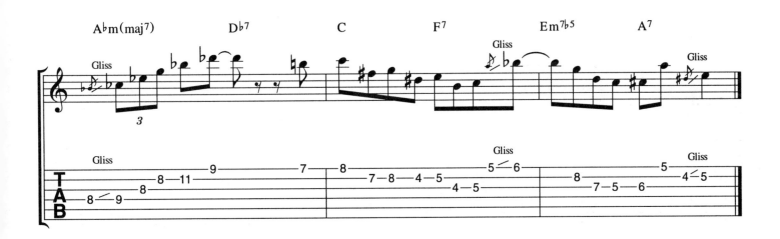

the way you look tonight

music by jerome kern
words by dorothy fields

Wes's storming solo on 'The Way You Look Tonight' is crammed with useful bebop vocabulary. Wes often uses groups of notes that move down in semitone steps, a device adopted by current players such as Pat Metheny. Wes plays very rhythmically here. You never hear just endless strings of quavers. The tempo is quite 'up', so slow the solo down and pick out some of the lines which catch your ear.

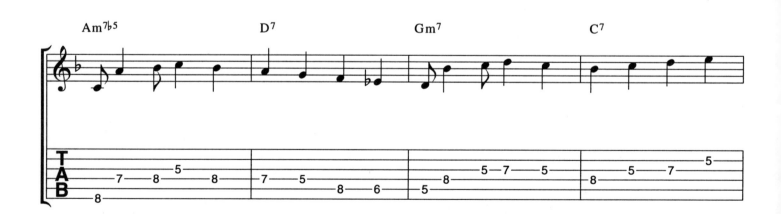

© copyright 1936 t.b. harms & company incorporated, usa
warner chappell music limited, 129 park street, london w1/
polygram music publishing limited, 47 british grove, london w4
all rights reserved
international copyright secured

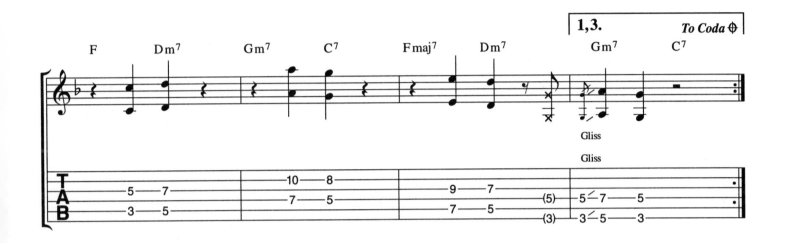

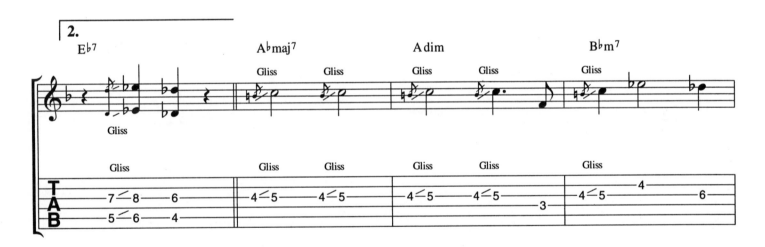

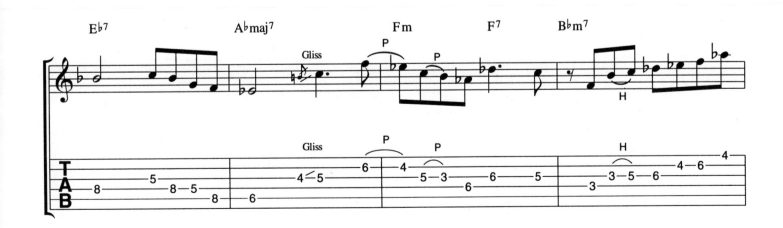

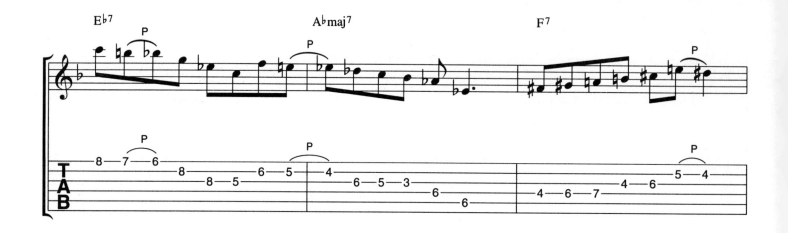

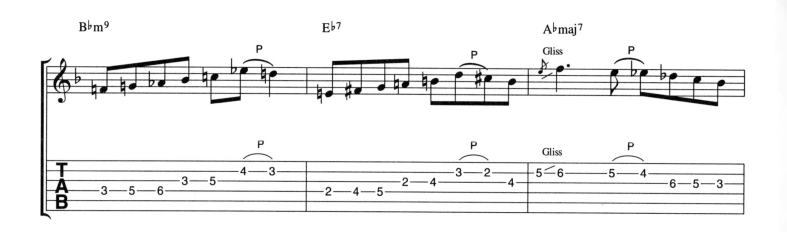

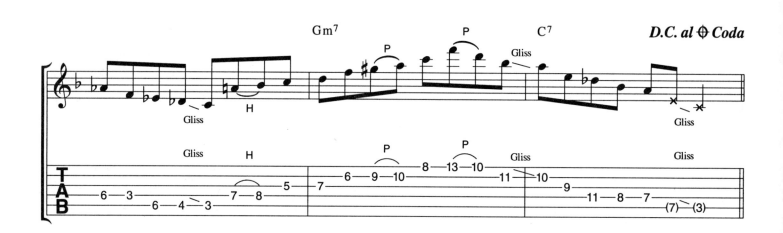

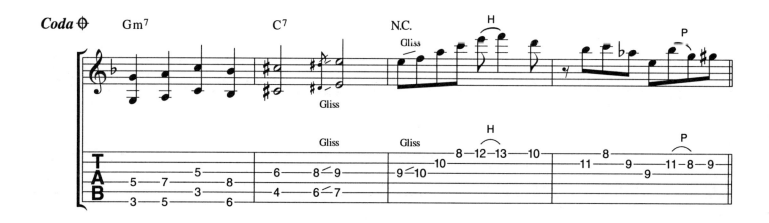

A Solo:

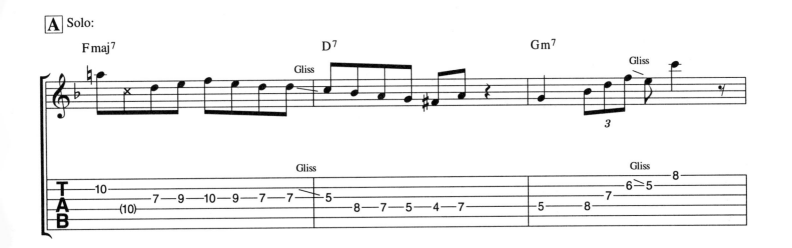

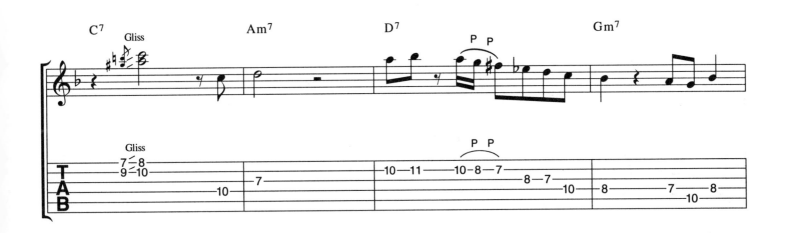

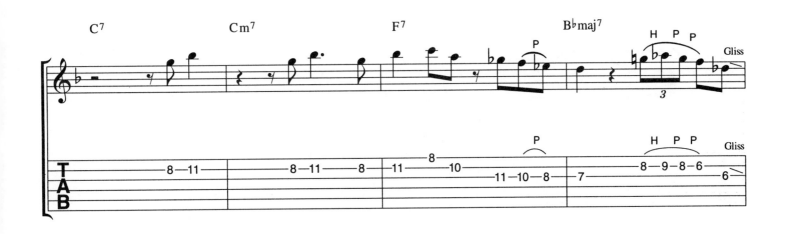

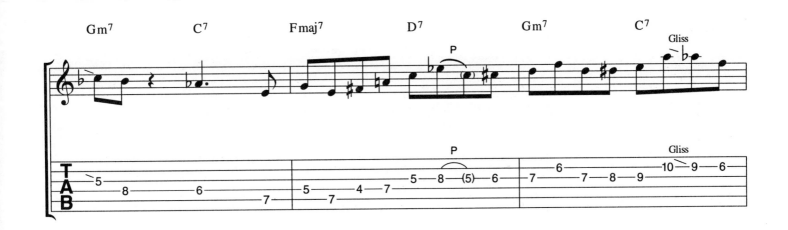

B

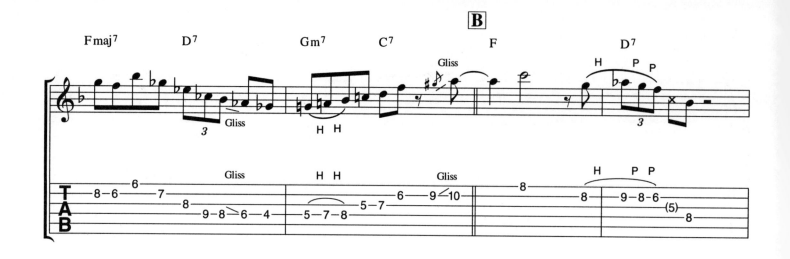

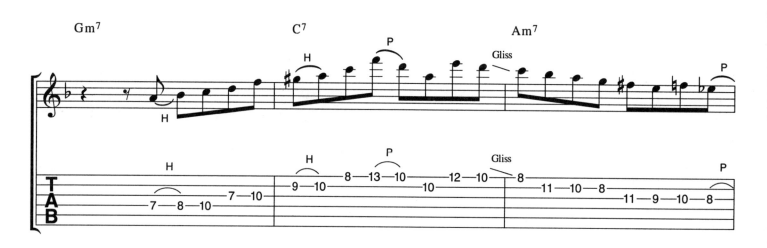

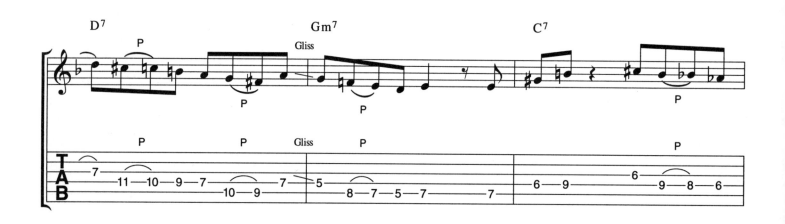

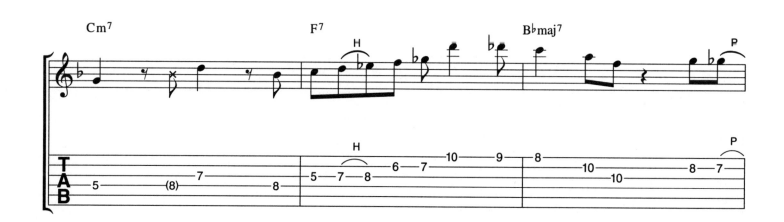

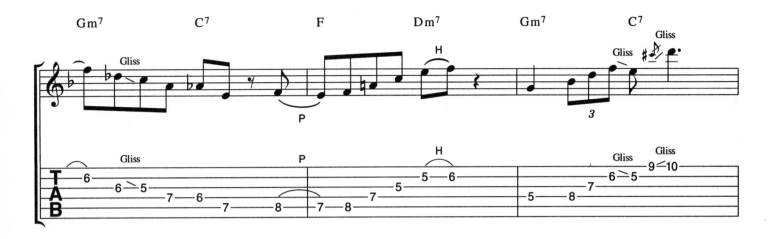

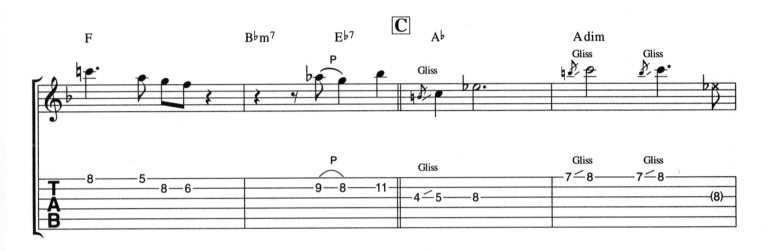

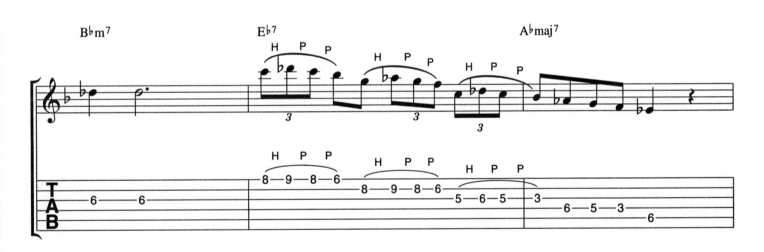

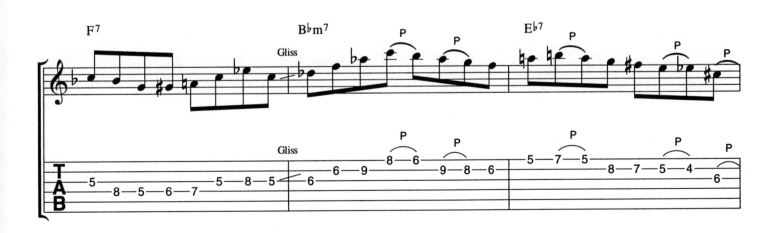

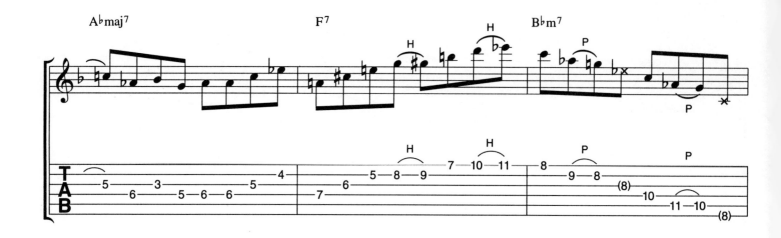

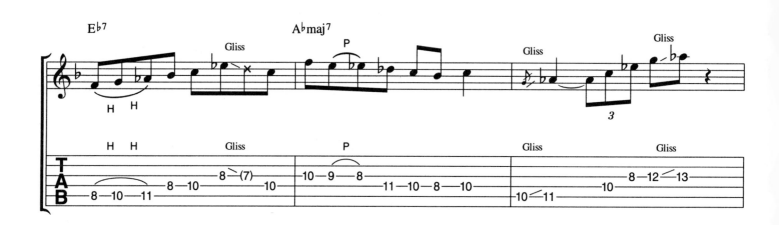

D

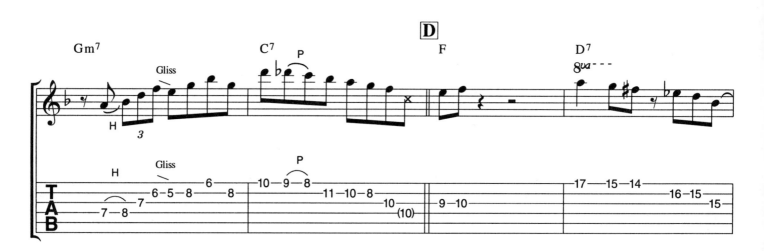

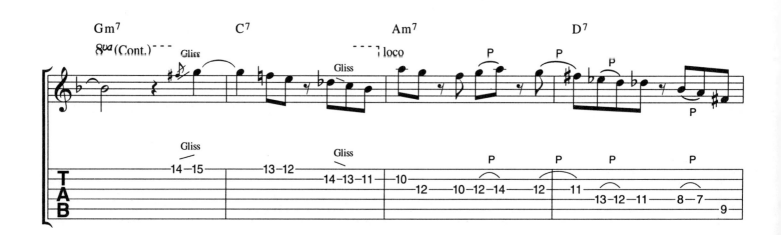

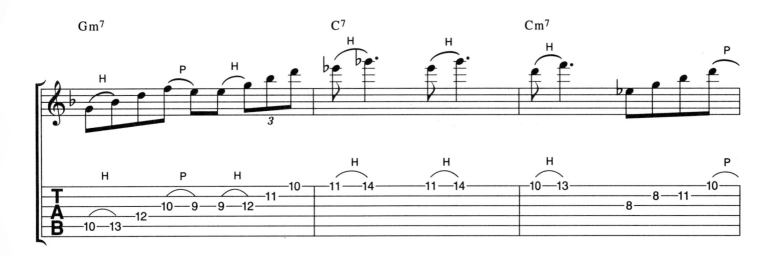

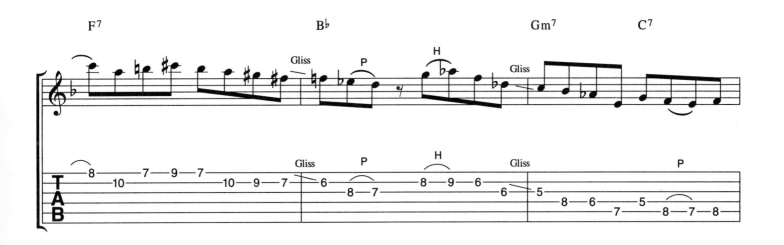

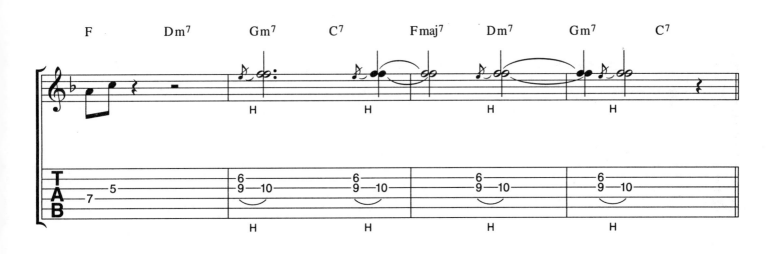

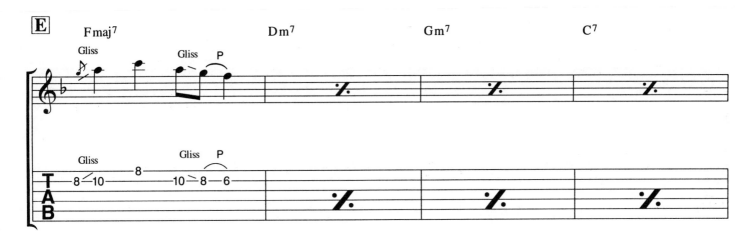

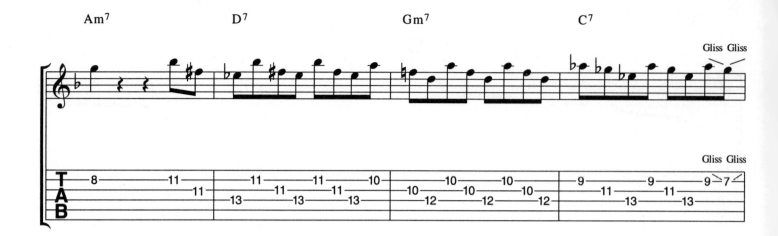

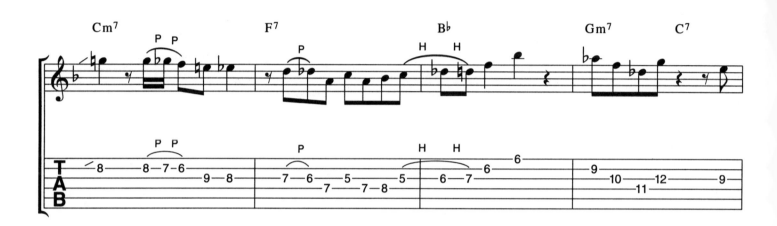

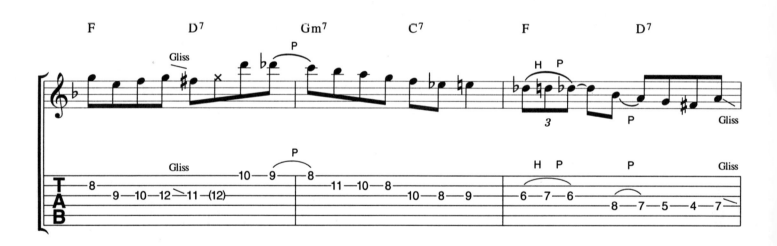

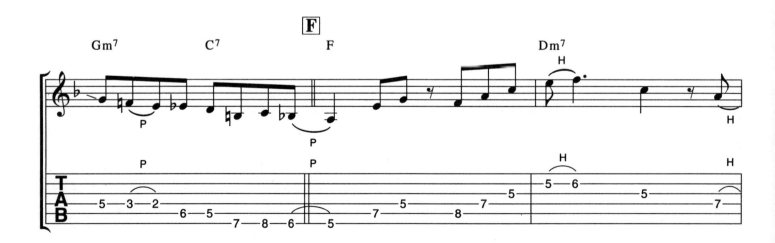

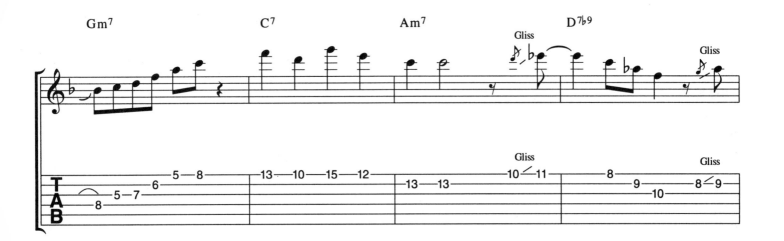

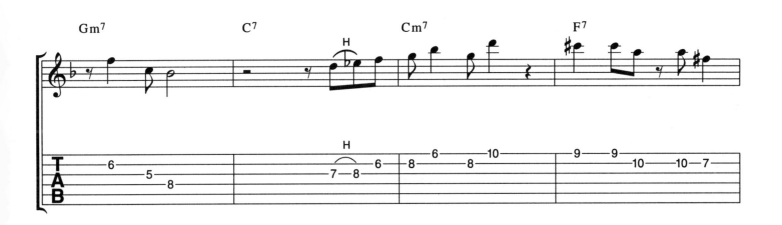

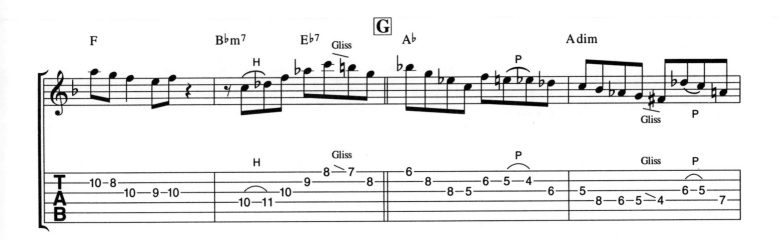

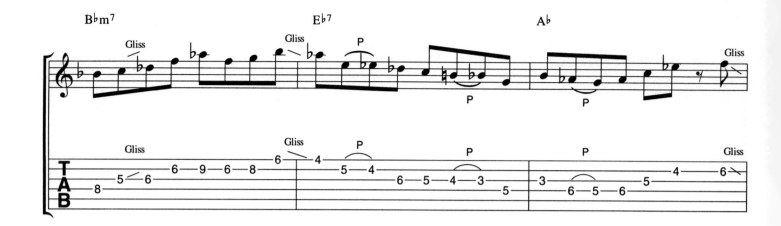

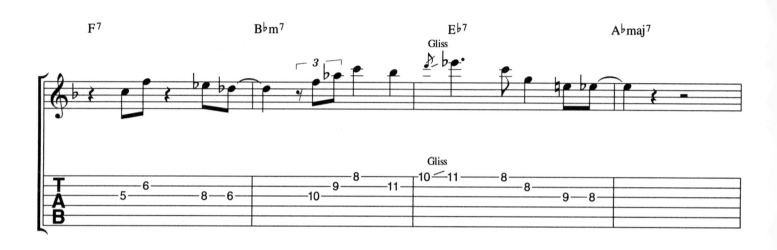

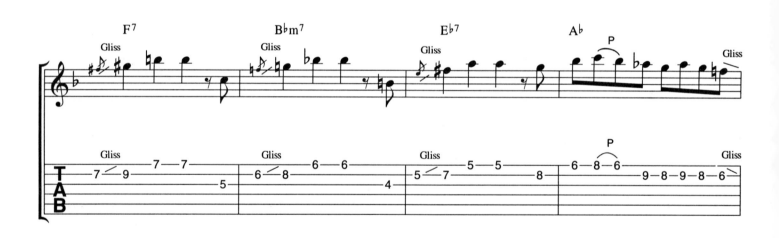

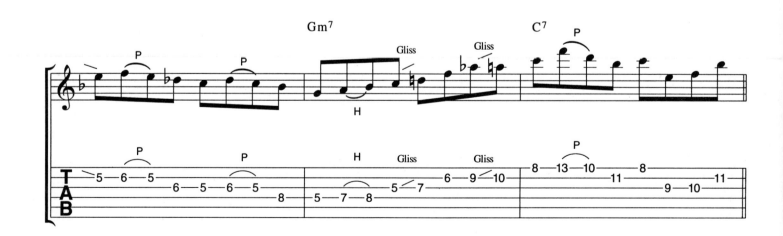

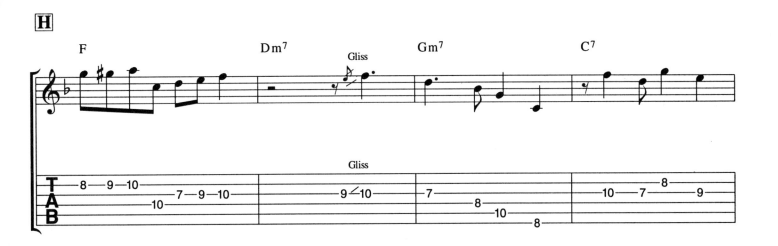

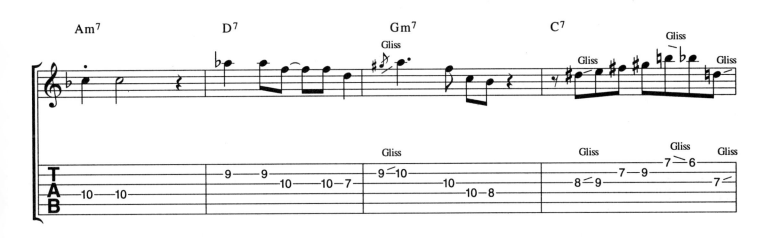

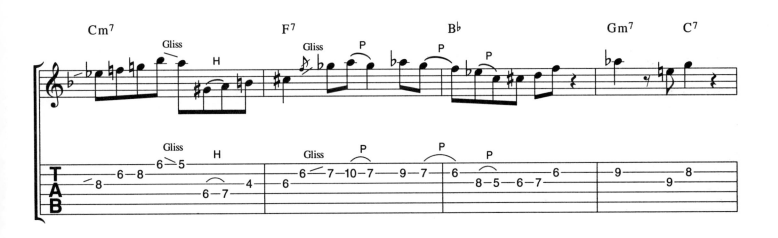

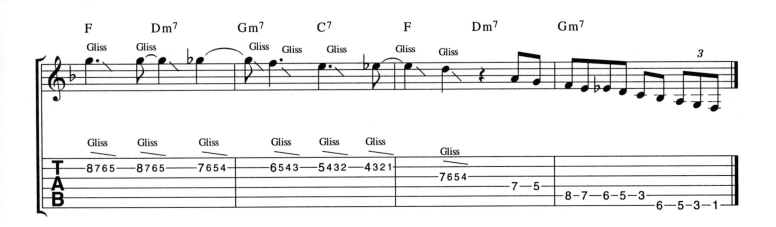

ecaroh

by horace silver

Wes's solo in this Horace Silver tune (the title is Horace spelled backwards) is a combination of simple bluesy melodic ideas and eighth-note bebop lines. There is quite a lot of useful jazz vocabulary in this solo. Try isolating some of the ideas and experimenting with them over other tunes. You'll notice that jazz standards are full of the same harmonic formulae, so get used to the idea of making the most of your materials. If an idea works over one set of chords, investigate where else you can use it. For instance, try looking for the same progression in another key.

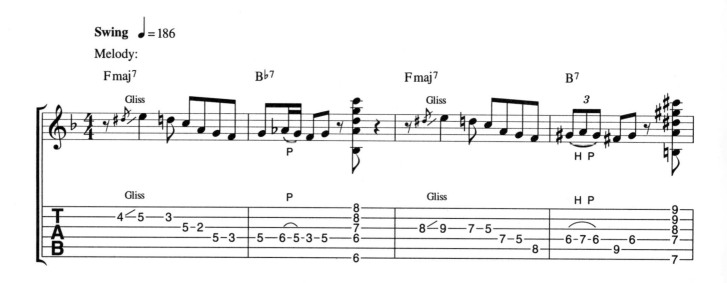

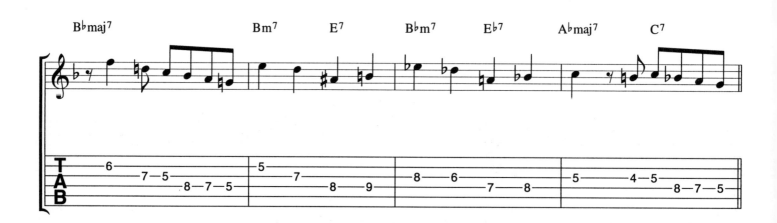

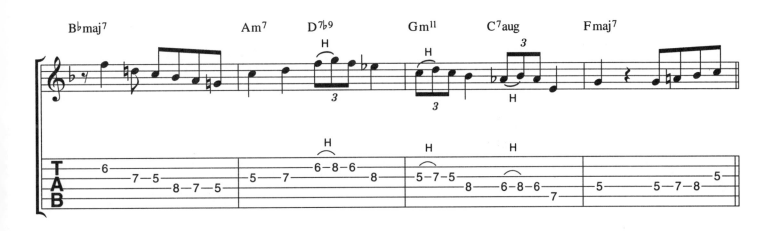

Straight eights

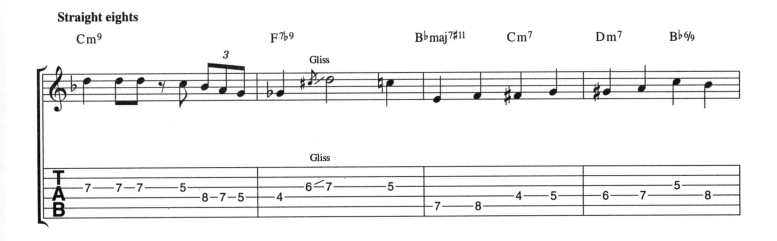

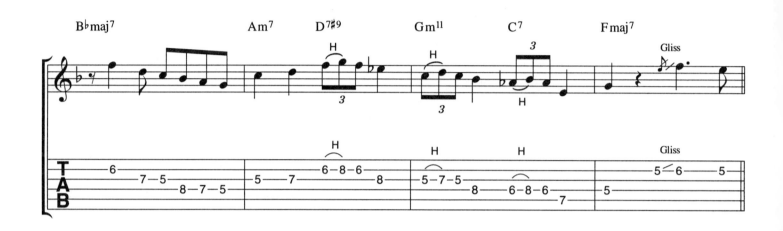

A Solo:

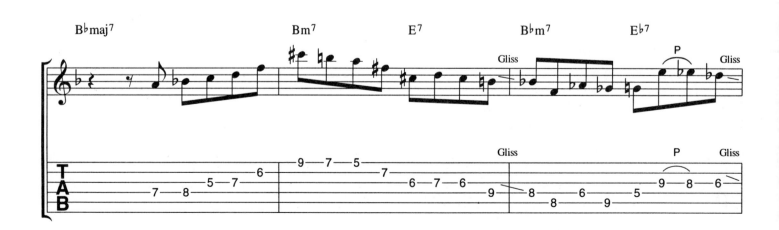

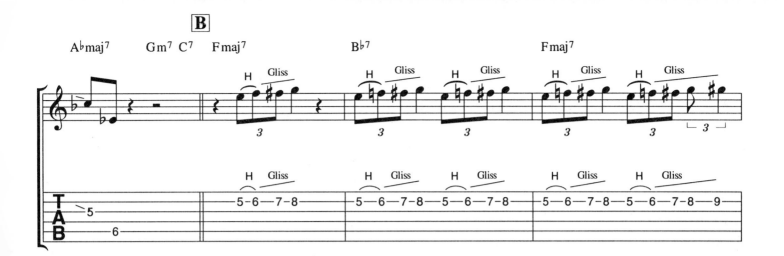

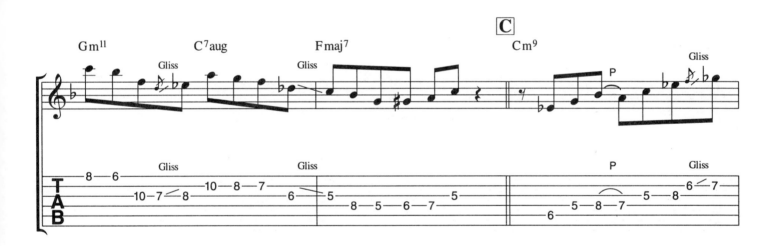

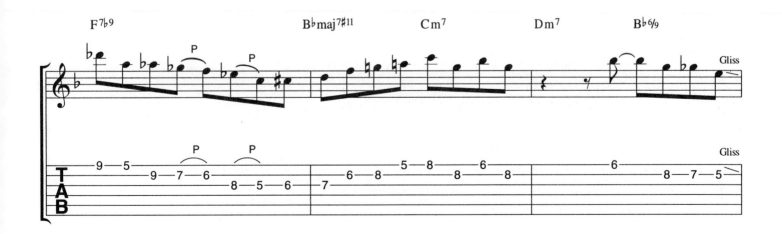

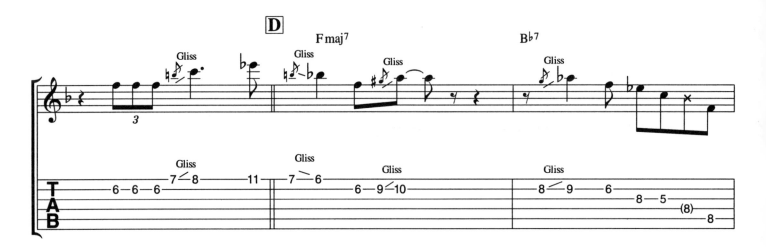

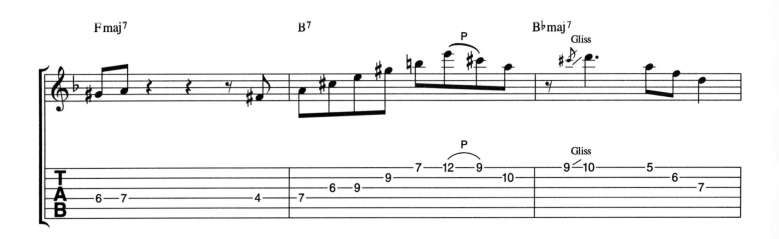

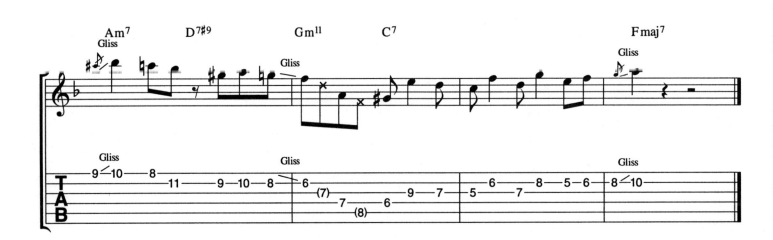

whisper not

words & music by benny golson

Wes plays the melody of Benny Golson's 'Whisper Not' almost completely in octaves and then continues right into the solo. If you're new to playing in octaves you could start by learning the solo in single notes only. Interestingly, playing in octaves forces us to think very melodically because it's basically such an awkward technique to use. There are some great voicings in the second section of the melody. Note the use of the natural 9th degree over the minor 7th flat 5 (e.g. the note F♯ over the Em7♭5). Also check out the way Wes uses chromatic notes and the ways in which he approaches chord tones (often from a semitone away).

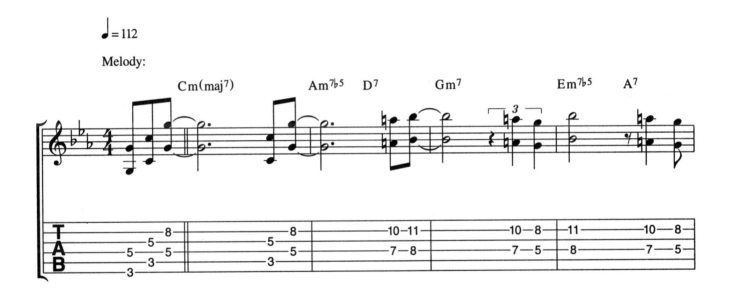

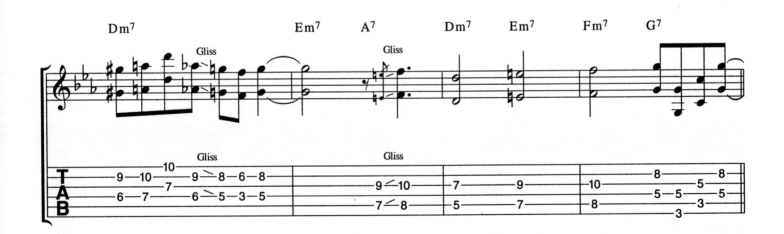

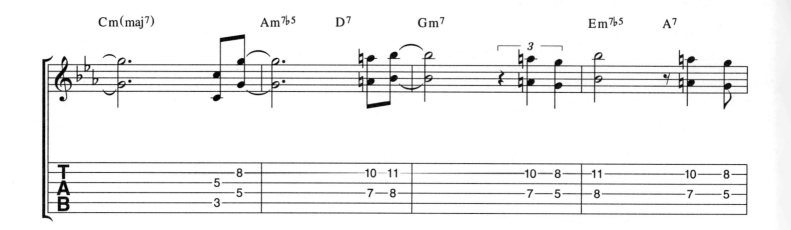

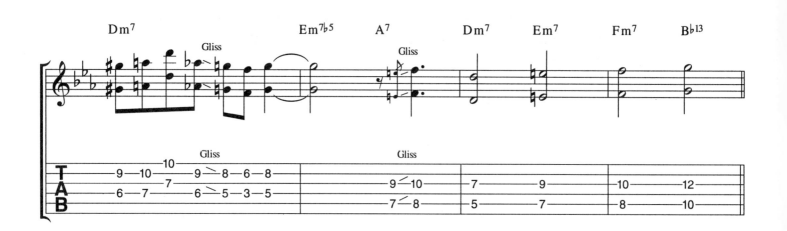

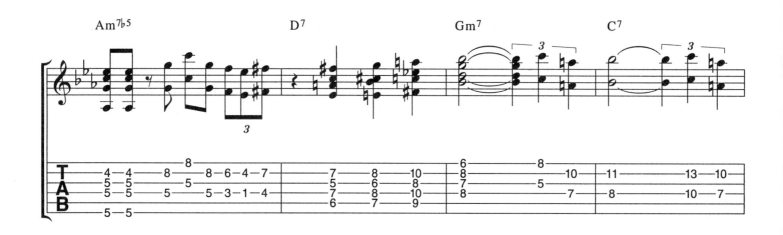

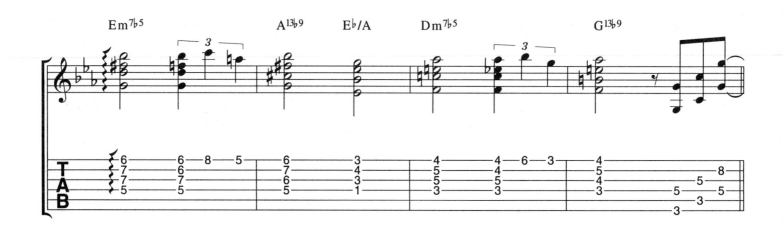

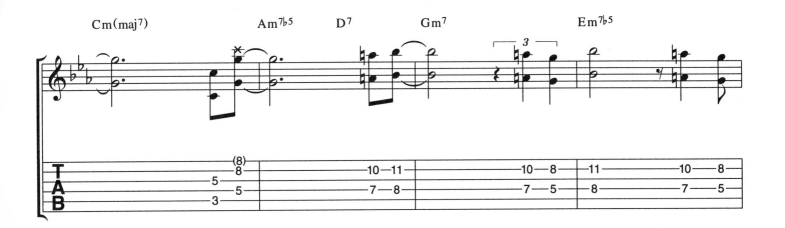

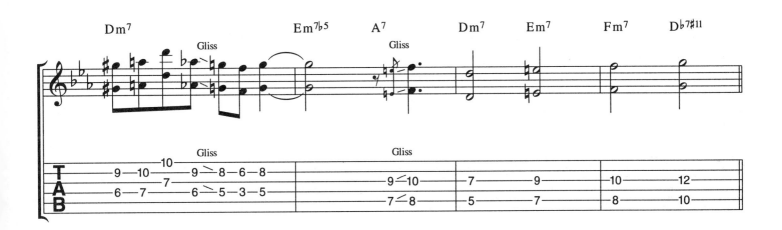

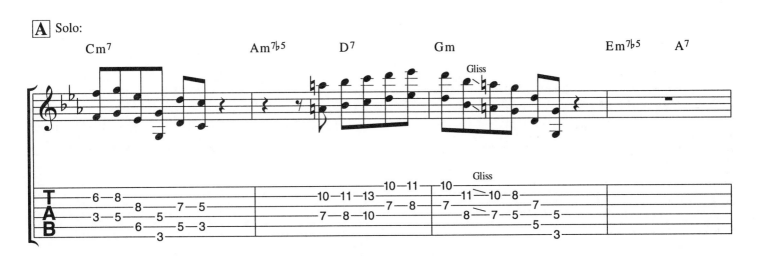

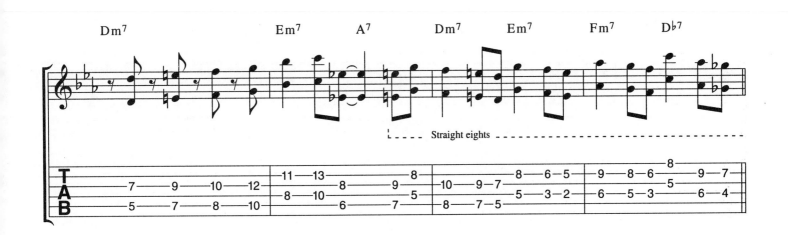

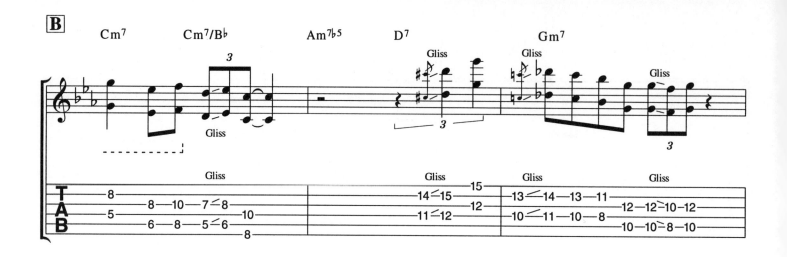

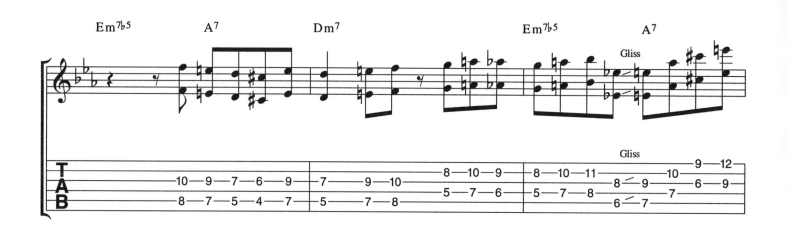

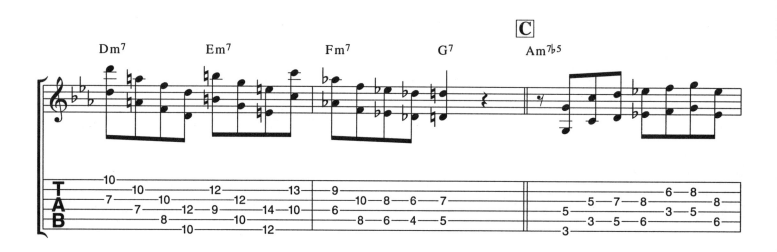

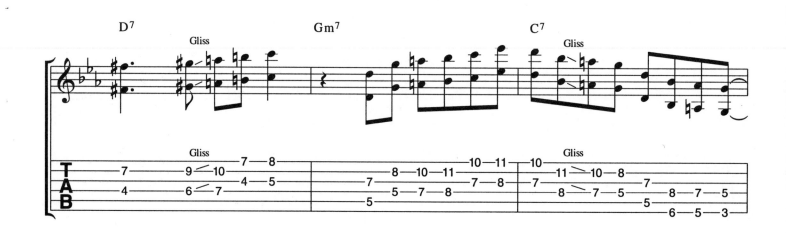

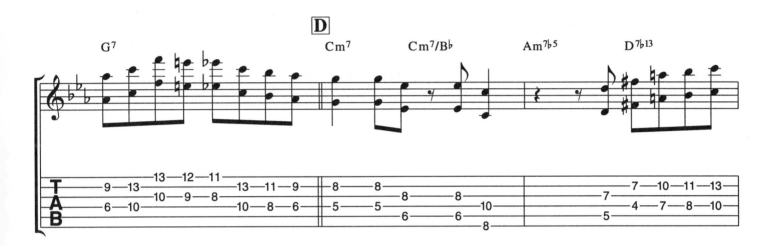

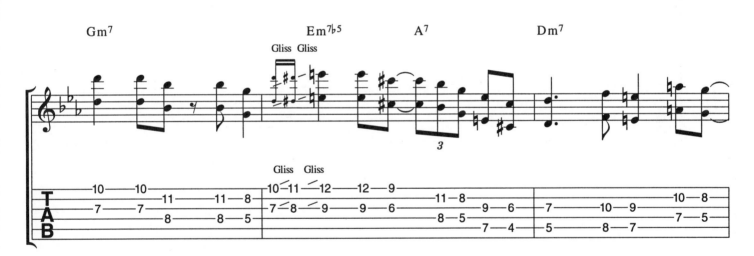

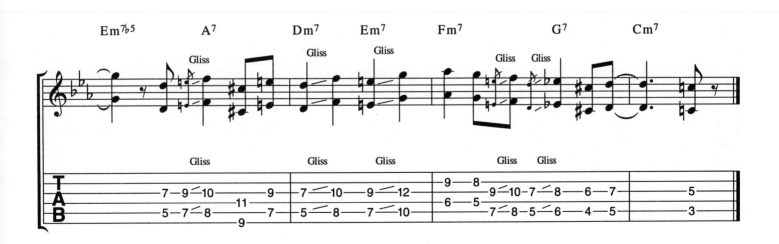

yesterdays

music by jerome kern
words by otto harbach

Wes's treatment of the melody in this Jerome Kern tune sounds simple, but you'll notice a few sly embellishments. The great jazz musicians all try to make the most of a melody, whereas you often hear less experienced players sounding as if the melody is just something you get past in order to get to the improvising. In the first eight-bar section note the use of 11th degrees over the dominant 7ths. See also the heavy use of the sharpened 11th degree over the 7th chords in the last 12 bars. Throughout the book you'll notice we've indicated only the basic chords for the tune – Wes often implies other harmonies. It's rather unfashionable these days to play in octaves but remember that Wes was breaking new ground when he did it. Don't switch off. Just check out the great lines he's playing!

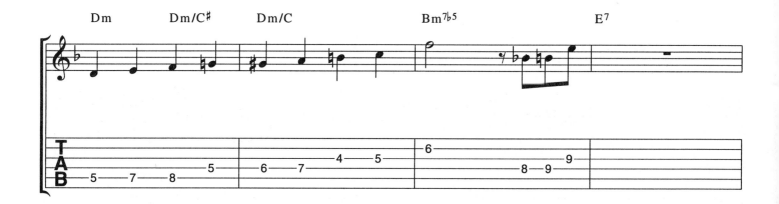

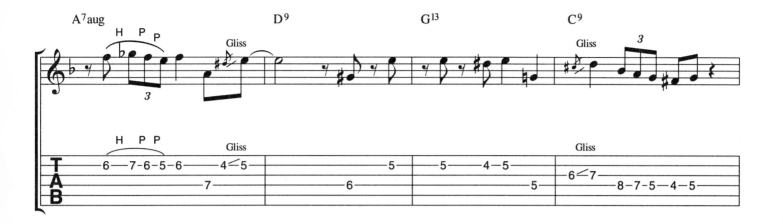

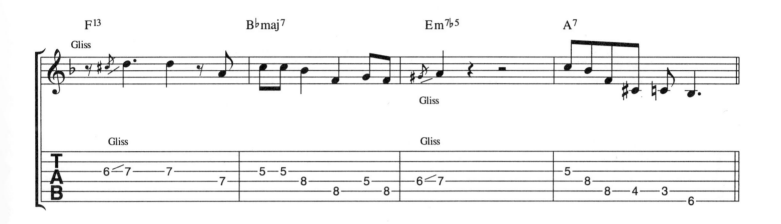

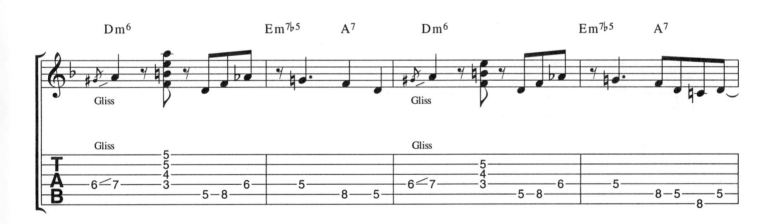

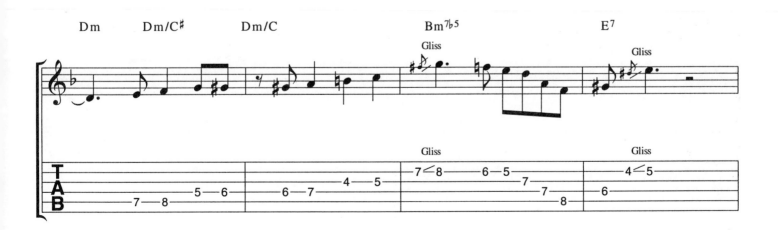

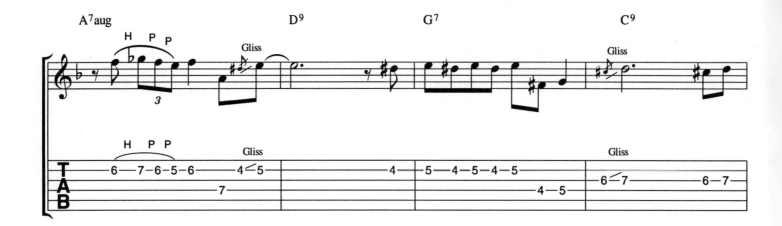

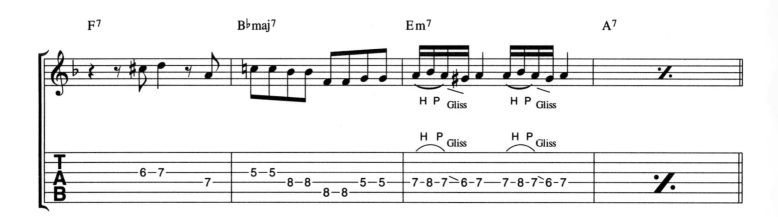

A Solo:

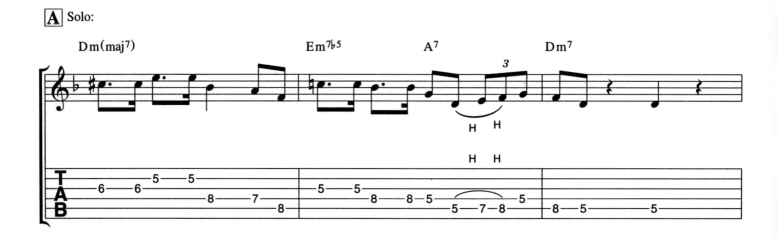

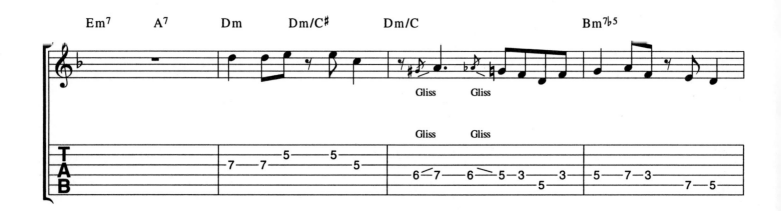

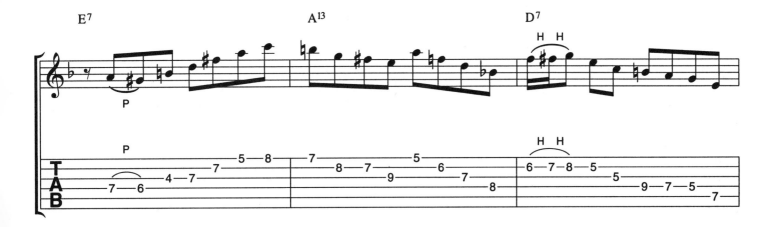

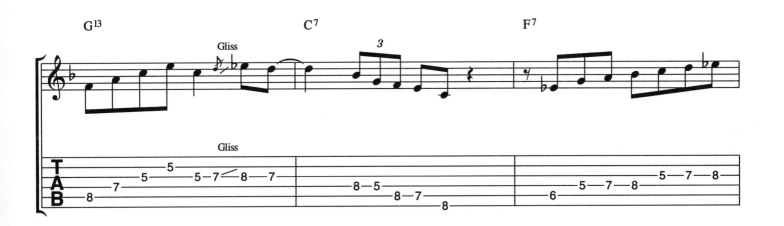

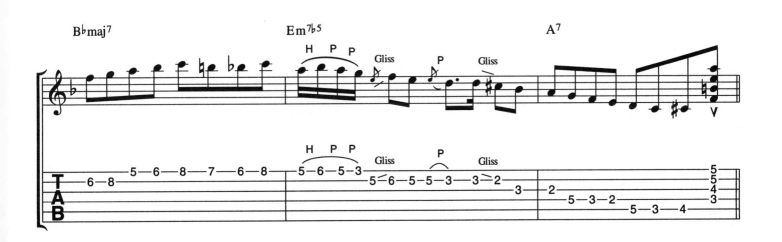

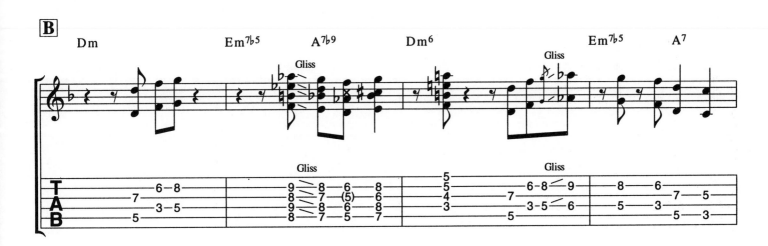

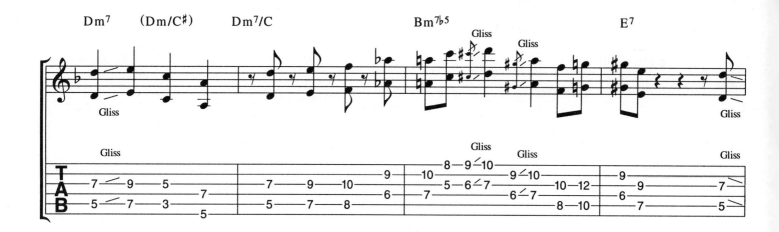

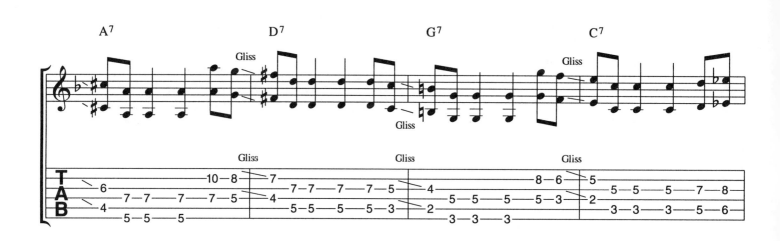

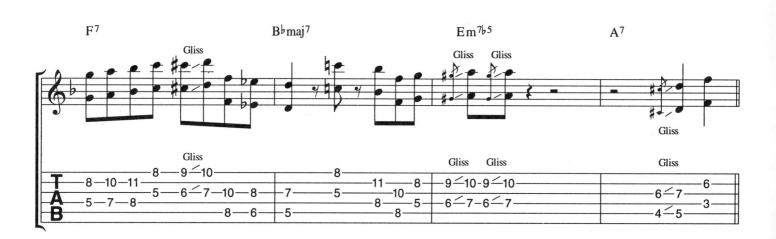

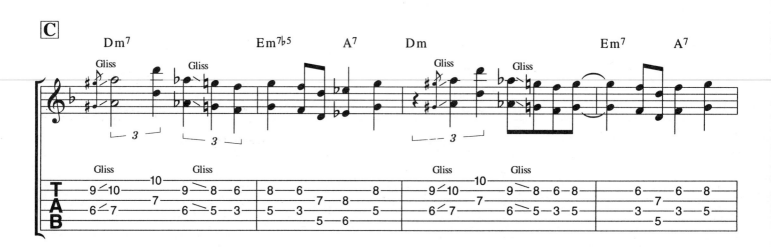

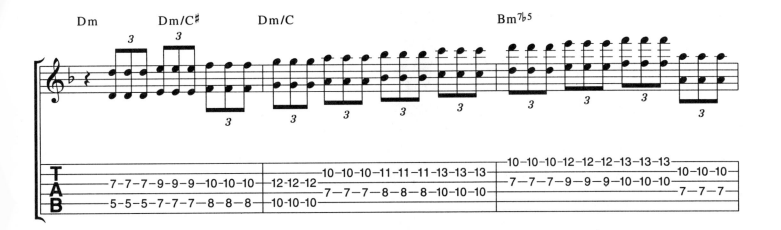

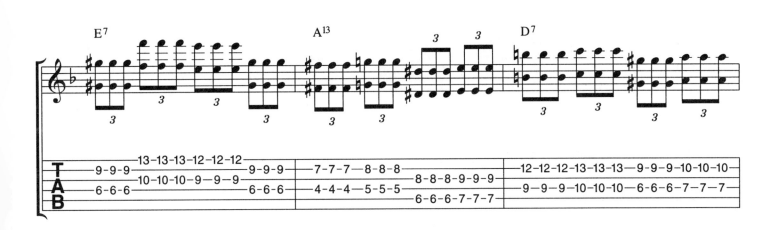

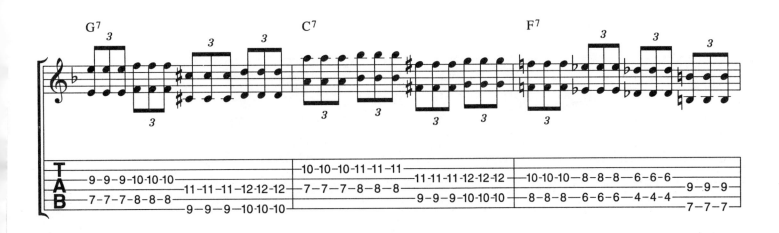

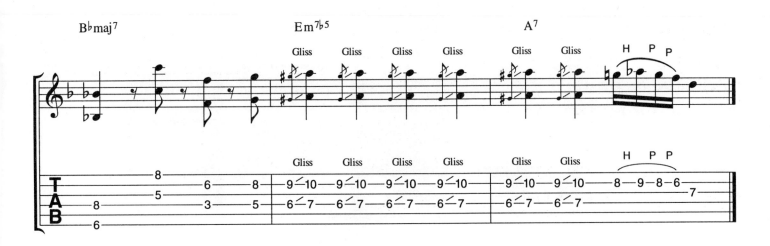

The Beatles

Enya

Phil Collins

Van Morrison

Bob Dylan

Sting

Paul Simon

Tracy Chapman

Eric Clapton

Pink Floyd

New Kids On The Block

Bryan Adams

Tina Turner

Elton John

Bee Gees   Whitney Houston   AC/DC

Bringing you the words

All the latest in rock and pop. Plus the brightest and best in West End show scores. Music books for every instrument under the sun. And exciting new teach-yourself ideas like "Let's Play Keyboard" - in cassette/book packs, or on video. Available from all good music shops.

and music

Music Sales' complete catalogue lists thousands of titles and is available free from your local music shop, or direct from Music Sales Limited. Please send a cheque or postal order for £1.50 (for postage) to:

Music Sales Limited
Newmarket Road,
Bury St Edmunds,
Suffolk IP33 3YB

Buddy

Five Guys Named Moe

Les Misérables

West Side Story

Phantom Of The Opera

Show Boat

The Rocky Horror Show

Bringing you the world's best music.